PROMENADE HOME

Promenade Home

Macrobiotics and Women's Health

By Gale Jack with Alex Jack

Foreword by Michio and Aveline Kushi

Japan Publications, Inc.

Published by Japan Publications, Inc., Tokyo and New York

Distributors:

UNITED STATES: *Kodansha International/USA, Ltd., through Harper & Row, Publishers, Inc., 10 East 53rd Street, New York, New York 10022.* SOUTH AMERICA: *Harper & Row, Publishers, Inc., International Department.* CANADA: *Fitzhenry & Whiteside Ltd., 195 Allstate Parkway, Markham, Ontario, L3R 4T8.* MEXICO AND CENTRAL AMERICA: *HARLA S. A. de C. V., Apartado 30–546, Mexico, 4, D. F.* BRITISH ISLES: *Premier Book Marketing Ltd., 1 Gower Street, London WCIE 6HA.* EUROPEAN CONTINENT (except Germany): *PBD Proost & Brandt Distribution bv, Strijkviertel 63, 3454 PK de Meern, The Netherlands.* GERMANY: *PBV Proost & Brandt Verlagsauslieferung, Herzstrasse 1, 5000 Köln, Germany.* AUSTRALIA AND NEW ZEALAND: *Bookwise International, 1 Jeanes Street, Beverley, South Australia 5007.* THE FAR EAST AND JAPAN: *Japan Publications Trading Co., Ltd., 1–2–1, Sarugaku-cho, Chiyoda-ku, Tokyo 101.*

First edition: July 1988

LCCC No. 87–82910
ISBN 0–87040–697–3

Printed in U.S.A.

Great it is to believe the dream
When we stand in youth by the starry stream.
But a greater thing is to fight life through
And say at the end, "The dream was true."
—Edwin Markham

Foreword

THE WORLD TODAY is experiencing a unique biological and spiritual crisis. In addition to the threat of nuclear war, the planet as a whole is facing loss of its natural environment and inhabitants. So many species of animals and plants are vanishing that we sometimes forget that the human family itself may perish through the spread of cancer, heart disease, mental illness, AIDS, and other degenerative and immuno-deficiency diseases. Hardly a household remains untouched by a life-threatening sickness.

While many factors have contributed to this decline, the underlying cause can be traced back to an unnatural way of living, especially an imbalanced way of eating that has separated us from the earth and sky and caused us to lose touch with our own minds, bodies, and spirits. Since the beginning of human culture and civilization, reverence for the soil and its products has been the cornerstone of wealth, happiness, and longevity.

Traditionally, the man went out into the fields or into society to provide for his family, while the wife prepared nourishing food for her husband and children. In this way, they complemented one another and created a strong, unified family. Along with grandparents and other relatives, they cooperated to build a cohesive family structure that was able to realize its common dream as well as weather life's inevitable ups and downs. Today, cooking, humanity's highest art, has become a menial occupation. Meat, poultry, dairy food, refined flour, canned goods, and other highly processed and artificially prepared foods have replaced humanity's staff of life: whole cereal grains. Homemade food, the center of the family for endless generations, has almost disappeared.

Family members no longer eat together. They experience several "food contacts" each day around the refrigerator, the television set, or the telephone. No wonder parents and children can't understand each other, and today the family is dying out.

Promenade Home is the warm-hearted story of one woman —a mother, wife, and schoolteacher—who was able to recover her health and happiness by returning to a traditional way of life and a more balanced way of eating. It is the first personal account offering macrobiotic insight into the common health and family problems of modern women. The author's pioneer heritage and Prairie/Southwest background help show that macrobiotics is not exclusively an Oriental philosophy but truly a universal way of life practiced by past generations in both East and West and that its principles are flexible and adaptable to all environments. The law (Order of the Universe) west of the Pecos is the same as that east of Kyoto.

Promenade Home is also a modern odyssey of applying yin and yang in daily life. As in Gale's case, thousands of friends around the world have had to rely on their own intuition and experience and "take two steps forward, then one step back" in restoring their health and well-being. When they began changing their way of eating, there were few teachers to support and guide them, and their associates were young and immature and still learning for themselves. After several years on her own, Gale studied at the Kushi Institute in Boston and at French Meadows Summer Camp in California. The description of her studies on the East and West Coasts, as well as her colorful portraits of many macrobiotic teachers, is a unique contribution to the history of our era. We strongly encourage everyone to follow Gale's example and periodically keep a diary. Such a journal is an invaluable tool for self-reflection and a treasure to be passed down to one's children and grandchildren.

After a long, winding journey, Gale took responsibility for her difficulties and entered upon the way to greater health and freedom. She returned to the native roots of the American heartland and learned to hear the voice of ancestral and parental wisdom. She is now spreading light to others through her wonderful meals, cooking classes, and work with schoolchildren, prisoners, and sick people. With her husband, Alex, her son, Jon, and her extended family of friends and relatives in Texas, Massachusetts, and around the planet, she is serving as a bright, shining example for One Peaceful World.

MICHIO and AVELINE KUSHI
Brookline, Massachusetts
January, 1988

Preface

Promenade, go two by two,
Promenade home like you always do.

I N THIS AGE OF ROCK AND ROLL and of dancing without
partners, some younger readers may not understand the
title of this book. "Promenade Home" is a square dance
call in which each couple goes counterclockwise around the
circle holding hands crosswise and returning to their home
position. After completing several turns around the dance
floor with other partners, everyone traditionally "promenades
home" at the end of the dance with their original partner and
returns to their starting place.

My life has been one not of moderation but of extremes. My
experiences have led me to mingle with the poor and the rich:
the most physically active—farmers and construction workers
—and the most gentle—artists and intellectuals. I have worked
with the strong and healthy and with those burdened with disease, poverty, and physical and mental deformity. I have been
attracted to both the God-fearing and the God-defying.

And in my own dance through life, I have at times felt confident and comfortable in guiding others and at other times
felt exhausted, depressed, deeply inferior, and in need of guidance and care myself.

For almost the first forty years of my life, there was no
middle road for me. Although I had risen to the peak of my
career professionally and enjoyed a glamorous social life, I
eventually became so sick and depressed that I no longer saw
life as a dance to be enjoyed but as an ordeal to be endured.

After my own personal health and judgment declined, my family collapsed.

Unfortunately, my experience has not been very different from that of millions of other modern women. Fortunately, all suffering is accompanied by the opportunity for greater happiness. The solution I adopted turned out not to be a new way —an esoteric Far Eastern teaching, though that was the way it was initially introduced to me—but an old way—a universal way of life similar to that followed by my parents, grandparents, and generations of past ancestors who helped settle our native American soil.

Macrobiotics enables me to live in a more moderate way. To the amazement of the many doctors, psychiatrists, and specialists I have gone to over the years, as well as my own family and friends, I recovered my health and happiness, and I have gone on to create harmony in a new family situation. There are still ups and downs to my life, and looking back I can only characterize my early practice of macrobiotics as extreme. But studying *yin* and *yang*—the two universal forces that comprise all phenomena—and applying them to cooking and daily life have set me free. I can now chart my own course through life and that of my family without being dependent on others.

Macrobiotics also helped me be a better schoolteacher and psychologist in the Texas school system. After I began eating brown rice and learning about yin and yang it was much easier to understand the behavior problems of the children who were referred to me. One couple, for example, came to see me about their son. They described how he would sneak downstairs after midnight and steal chocolate-covered cherries and other sweets from the kitchen and how troubled they felt when they'd wake to find an empty candy box behind the sofa. At other times he would beat his head against the wall in his room. They were very upset at his "stealing" and his "disobedience" and wanted to know what was wrong with him.

To their surprise, I inquired about the boy's intake of meat and salt. I found that not only was he eating meat every day (which is already high in sodium) but also that he sprinkled raw salt on it from the salt shaker at the table. It was making him incredibly tight—what in macrobiotics we call extreme *yang*—so he couldn't keep still. In addition, the salt and meat were attracting him to chocolate-covered cherries and other strong relaxing or expansive foods—what we call extreme *yin*. It was not a question of willful disobedience or dishonesty but satisfying an underlying craving and biological imbalance.

I took a yellow sheet of paper and right there in the conference explained to the parents briefly about yin and yang. I listed the most yang items on one side of the page and the most yin on the other and explained why their son was being attracted to "yin." I explained how they could eliminate the source of their son's problem and help him a lot by managing his diet. He was hitting his head against the wall because he had eaten so much beef, chicken, and other meats, as well as chips, spreads, and other convenience foods high in salt, in addition to salting everything at the table.

They seemed perplexed that I spoke of food and wasn't a doctor. Whether they followed my suggestions or not, I never found out as my time in that position was short-lived.

On another occasion, a young student was referred to me. He was basically alert and active but wasn't getting his work done in time and was always day-dreaming and a little spacy. During our conversation, I found he was eating bananas every day after school. Bananas grow in the tropics and are the staple food of monkeys and chimpanzees. They are not suitable for daily consumption in temperate climates such as most of the United States. Bananas' strong upward energy—the result of the earth's rotation at the equator—causes our minds to become too relaxed for concentration and serious study. A small volume of fruit, locally grown and in season, is an appropriate part of a balanced diet. I recommended that instead of bananas the boy be given apples, pears, berries, or melon.

Millions of schoolchildren (including my own teenage son who lives with his father and step-mother) have problems like this, yet they are labeled "learning disabled," "handicapped," "retarded," or "delinquent." Declining SAT scores can be directly correlated with the rise of junk food in the nation's schools, but something so basic as food quality is never considered, much less taught, by modern educators.

I'm especially grateful to my mother whose experience at the hands of modern medicine later made it an undesirable alternative for me. I am also grateful to my son, Jon, whose trust in me and the sound of his "Hey, Mom," gave me strength to recover from my difficulties and helps keep alive my dream of a unified family. I will also be forever grateful to Michio and Aveline Kushi for their inspiration and guidance and to Herman and Cornellia Aihara and other macrobiotic teachers and friends who have encouraged me along the way. I'd like to express my deepest gratitude to my husband, Alex. Without his help and daily prompting, this book would still be in the embryonic stage. For photographs and family records, I appreciate the assistance of my sister, Dot, and my cousins, Eugene and Mary Fields. Finally, I am thankful to Mr. Iwao Yoshizaki and Mr. Yoshiro Fujiwara, President and Vice-President respectively, of Japan Publications, Inc. for their support and encouragement. This project has truly been a meeting of the Far East and Wild West.

The square dance call "Promenade Home" is a metaphor for the spiral course of a happy, healthy, and peaceful life. After many adventures and separations, we discover our true dream, reach our destination, and find that we have returned to our origin. Yin and yang resume their proper places in perfect harmony, and we and the dance of life became one.

GALE JACK
Dallas, Texas
October, 1987

Contents

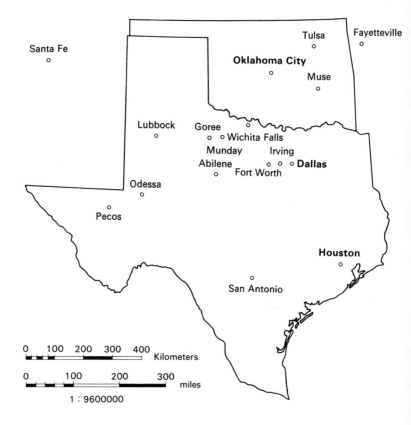

1.

Those Oklahoma Hills

Down in the valley, the valley so low,
Late in the evening, heard a train blow;
Heard a train blow, love, heard a train blow,
Late in the evening, heard a train blow.

OUTHEASTERN OKLAHOMA is a land of green hills, shady
valleys, tranquil rivers, and teeming wildlife. Opening up
to the grass-covered, wind-swept prairie, the area was the
oldest settled region of the Territory, ancestral hunting
grounds of the Cherokee and Choctaw Indians whose term for
themselves, *Okla Homa*, or "Red Man," became the name of the
entire state. An early English naturalist who visited this virgin
bower described it as "beautiful almost as the fanciful Elysium
. . . now enamelled with flowers . . . Serene and charming as
the blissful regions of fancy."

By the end of the 19th century, America's westward march
ended. Oklahoma became the last frontier. In a series of fabled
land runs beginning in 1889, thousands of families lined up to
cross the Arkansas, Kansas, and Texas borders to stake a claim
to the last free homesteads on the North American continent.
Gliding through the waves of tall grasses that blanketed much
of the former Indian Territory, the billowing canvas-covered
wagons of the pioneers resembled sailing ships.

Spiraling into the nation's center were men and women from
all cultures, backgrounds, and walks of life. Farmers collided
with cowboys and ranchers. Whites rubbed shoulders with
Indians, and native agricultural societies found themselves
adjacent to buffalo-hunting tribes from the Plains. Northerners

met Southerners, and former Union and Confederate soldiers found themselves neighbors. Emancipated blacks faced former plantation-owning whites. Recent immigrants from European coal mines and factories encountered frontiersmen whose ancestors had already cleared much of the country. Republicans met Democratics, Protestants joined Catholics, and those who believed in the gold standard patronized the same General Store as advocates of free silver.

Despite these differences, the newcomers had more in common than they had in opposition. Like those who had come before them, the new settlers sought more fertile soils, better opportunities for their children, and a fresh start. Laying down new roots, many of these first families prospered. New towns and cities sprang up overnight. Fields were planted, houses built, newspapers launched, and elections held. In the southeast, cotton and corn were the main crops. The central and western parts of Oklahoma, former crossroads for longhorn cattle driven north from Texas to railheads in Kansas, turned to wheat farming, livestock breeding, and—by the turn of the new century—to oil. Tulsa, a former Creek village, became the oil capital of the world, with more millionaires per capita than New York or San Francisco.

The mood of this time was captured by the *New York Times* in colorful reports on a '20's gubernatorial inauguration:

> The world's greatest barbecue, celebrating the inauguration of Governor Walton, in which thousands of beeves, reindeer, buffalo, bear, antelope, opossums, and countless numbers of sheep, hogs, rabbits, turkeys and chickens were cooked over a mile of trenches, began shortly after 1 o'clock today, following a mammoth parade and public inaugural of Walton before the joint bodies of the Legislature. . . .
>
> It was a scene such as Oklahoma had never witnessed before. The throng formed in eager lines before the serving stands as barbecue assistants began handing out great chunks of beef, buffalo, bear, and reindeer meat. Bread sliced and piled high like cotton bales began to shrink under the onslaught.

Giant coffee urns, each holding 10,000 gallons, and heated by
a steam engine, likewise became the Mecca of the thousands who,
as they received meat and bread, went on to complete their menu
with a cup of steaming coffee.

Following the parade and barbecue were a clog-dancing
contest, Black cakewalk, Indian war dance, old-time fiddlers'
contest, and a barn dance. The festivities concluded with a
boisterous square dance spread through the four floors of the
the state capitol.

Within a decade after World War I, the oil bubble burst.
Grain and livestock prices plunged, debts mounted, and homesteads were foreclosed. As oil fell from $3.75 a barrel to 15
cents by the beginning of the 1930s, thousands were thrown
out of work and banks failed. Meanwhile, a generation of
wasteful farming practices and cultivation of marginal lands
resulted in widespread soil erosion and environmental imbalance. Recurring cycles of drought, flood, wind storm, and
extreme temperatures struck the region, giving rise to tremendous natural calamities. Coupled with economic and cli-
matic dislocations, the arrival of the automobile, moving
pictures and radio, and bootleg whiskey undermined traditional
centers of family life such as the home, church, and school-
house. Pessimism replaced optimism, unemployment and
strikes supplanted hard work and industry, and violence born
of unfulfilled dreams became a way of life.

Though the depression of the 1930s was nation-wide, it
seemed to hit hardest in Oklahoma and surrounding areas.
Tremendous wind storms turned the geographical center of the
country into a Dust Bowl, and the era came down in American
mythology and legend as one of the greatest periods of hardship and difficulty since the landing of the Pilgrims.

Temperatures rose and fell 60 to 75 degrees in a few hours.
Corn and wheat shriveled with the arrival of sudden arctic
winds, rain ceased to fall for up to six months at a time, and
sudden hailstorms, flash floods, and torrential rains left the land

scarred. Coupled with occasional earthquakes and migrations of hungry rabbits and grasshoppers, the awesome onset of huge "rollers"—moving walls of blowing dust that blocked out the sunlight—left humans, animals, and crops devastated, dazed, and bewildered in a modern plague of Biblical proportions.

Birth in Muse

I came into the world on May 12, 1939, toward the close of this tragic chapter in American history. My birthplace, Muse, Oklahoma, was located in the southeastern part of the state in hilly terrain near the Kiamichi River. In Choctaw, *Kiamichi* means "refuge." The surrounding mountains of the same name offered a measure of protection from the fury of nature that disregard for the land and the spread of modern civilization seemed to have unleashed.

My father, James (Jim) Monroe Fields was born in Arkansas on August 15, 1892. George Washington Fields, my grandfather, was born in Georgia in 1847 or 1848 and passed away about 1911. Martha Jane Gibson, his third wife and my grandmother, was born on May 12, 1866 (the same month and day as me) in Polk County, Arkansas and died in 1906. Her maiden name was McBride, and she was apparently of Choctaw origin.

Just when and from where the Fields family first came to America remains unknown. Like many settlers in the new land, Daddy's kin looked forward, not backward, and old ties were quickly forgotten. Fields is an English country name. It's possible they came in one of the waves of immigration that followed upheavals in traditional agricultural life sparked by the Industrial Revolution. There was also said to be some Indian ancestry on father's side, but like so many things of the past, this has been difficult to verify.

George Washington and Martha Jane Fields had eight children. Daddy was the third of six sons and had two sisters. There were also four children from Granddaddy's two earlier marriages, but I don't know how many of them were living with the family when my father was growing up. By all accounts, the Fields' brothers were rough and high-tempered. All served in the First World War and returned to southeastern Oklahoma, where Grandfather Fields had brought the family in a covered wagon in one of the first pioneer treks about 1895.

In Muse, the Fields boys earned the reputation of being "fighting knives." According to family tradition, one of my uncles resettled in Texas, spurring his horse ahead of a sheriff pursuing him from Oklahoma. His offense has not been recorded. But at that era, there was widespread dissatisfaction in Oklahoma and Arkansas among sharecroppers and small farmers. Members of grass-roots organizations such as the Grange, the Wheel—named after Ezekiel's flaming chariot in the Bible—and the National Farmers Alliance were often detained because of their populist views. My uncle may have run afoul of the law for something less idealistic such as making moonshine—illegal whiskey. Prohibition was never entirely repealed from wide areas of the South and Southwest, and clashes between country folk and revenuers were legion.

In 1917, on the eve of America's entry into World War I, Dad and his brother Sam married Dessie Lee and Essie Duvall, twin sisters from West Texas. Born on August 5, 1901 in Eastland, Mother was nine years younger than Daddy. Her father, Jonathan Larenzie Duvall, came from Dutch or French ancestry, and her mother, Margaret Ida Moore, was evidently of English background. In addition to her twin sister, Mother had several older brothers who, like the Fields boys, were renowned for their fighting spirit and heavy drinking.

After serving with an infantry regiment in France, Dad returned home to farming and to carpentry. Like many men from the rural South, he worked as a tenant farmer and supplemented what he could provide for his growing family by hunting and fishing. Because of his knowledge of the land, he was often hired as a guide by others who came into the area to

hunt. He also worked on road construction for the W.P.A.—
President Franklin Roosevelt's Works and Projects Adminis-
tration—and served with the C.C.C.—the Civilian Conser-
vation Corps—planting trees, improving irrigation, and
generally helping to reclaim the land. On Saturdays, Dad
would also cut hair for people. He was a natural barber and
enjoyed trimming locks and beards, whether he was paid or not.

Mother was fifteen years old when she married, and Daddy
was twenty-four. After the war, Daddy filed for veterans'
benefits and received a small monthly stipend for mumps and
tuberculosis which he came down with while in the service. He
also claimed atrophy of the testicles, but the birth of a daughter,
Dorothy (Dot), in 1921, proved this a misdiagnosis. The
young couple went on to have four sons—Williard, M.J., and
the twins, Leborn (Big Hoke) and Cleborn (Little Hoke).

The youngest member of the family, I was born in a small
house on Harricane Hill, several miles outside of town. The
site owed its name to tremendous electrical storms and tem-
pests during the Dust Bowl era that nearly scared to death the
few people in that part of the valley. My birth was attended by
a midwife from Big Cedar who had been fetched by my father.

Shortly after my birth, we moved to larger quarters off
Muse's one and only main street. We lived in an old white
frame house, whose heat was provided by a fireplace and a
woodburning stove in the kitchen. The food was cooked on
this stove, and it was also used to heat a metal iron for ironing
clothes. We had no electricity and used kerosene lamps. Water
came from a hand-dug well, and fresh milk was kept in jugs
in the well.

Our family's staple was corn. Of course, we enjoyed it fresh
from the fields, boiled on the cob. But like most people in the
South and Southwest, we ate it primarily in the form of cornbread. We didn't have a grinder at home, but there were one or
two in the valley. From time to time, Mother would take the
newly harvested ears to a neighbor's and have her corn ground
in return for a small portion of the crop. She also made her

own hominy and grits, using lye to take the skins off the corn in an old black pot.

As sharecroppers, our family had to give one-third of our corn and one-quarter of our cotton to the landowner. Cotton was the main cash crop in this part of Oklahoma, and we hung on to it as much as possible. Merchants in town carried farm families from year to year, waiting to collect until after the cash crop was sold. Most of the time, we had no money and relied on barter. For example, the postman would give us a 3 cent stamp in return for three eggs.

In a good year, Daddy might clear $175, with which he would buy wheat flour, oatmeal, cloth, and other basics as well as canned goods, sugar, coffee, and other extras. All of our produce came fresh from the garden, especially sweet potatoes, turnips, black-eyed peas, and watermelons. We also had our own chickens and eggs.

When we had a little bit of money to spend, we would go to Talihina, about twenty miles away. Talihina, a former missionary settlement in the valley of the Winding Stair Mountains, had grown into a large town of nearly two thousand inhabitants with the coming of the railroad. Indeed, its name, in Choctaw, meant "Iron Road." There my parents would select the provisions they needed, and we children might be treated to a moving picture show or an ice cream soda.

The most delicious food I remember during my years in Oklahoma was wild blackberries and huckleberries. After being picked and put in large pails, they would be canned to last through the winter, when fresh fruit was unavailable or too expensive. Once Mother had some berries sitting on the top of a closet (closets were not built into the rooms then), and Big Hoke climbed up to get some and knocked off a bucket, spilling berries everywhere. Boy, was Mom upset! One Christmas, Uncle Frank sent us a box of canned fruit, nuts, and candy. As we had nothing like that ourselves, it was gratefully received.

As children, we were given baths in metal tubs, called #2 tubs or #3 tubs, according to the size. (My father made home-

made beer in another tub.) The tubs were filled with water
and left in the sun to warm. In the summer we were bathed
outdoors. My brothers were bathed first and then me. In fact,
it seemed my whole life, my brothers were first and I was last,
if I got to do it at all.

My oldest brother, Willard (whom we all called Bill) was at
home then. I used to sit in his lap on the front porch wearing a
dress with matching panties made of feed sack. Feed sack was
the fabric that flour and other dry goods came in. We'd buy it
in twenty-five-pound bags, and when a bag was empty, the
seams were removed, and the fabric could then be used for
aprons, cup towels, dresses, and other items. I felt so secure
sitting there with the sun shining, feeling all was well with the
world.

My brothers didn't share this same sense of security with
Bill. He seemed to be a self-appointed sergeant around the
house, taking charge of the younger ones.

My sister Dot was seventeen years older and already in
high school when I was born. When not playing basketball or
in school, she was helping Mom with us younger children.
Once Uncle Sam and Aunt Essie had a square dance at their
home, and children from the whole valley came in the old
school bus. It was one of the highlights of Dot's growing up.

My closest playmate was cousin Edward. Once his older
brother came home from the navy with a beer stein filled with
pennies. He'd brought these for Edward, and I thought they
were rich! Edward and I were about the same age. We had no
toys from the store. Instead, we played with blocks of wood in
the sandpile or stick horses and stilts that my brothers had
made. I remember some men were once working on a screen.
They had it spread over two saw horses and had scattered nails
on the grass around them. It was a hot, sunny day. I picked up
the nails for them, and as an expression of gratitude, they gave
me a nickel. I bought a tall, cool orange soda pop. I still
remember how refreshing it was. I'm told I threw a hammer at
Edward once and hit him in the head. At an early age I learned
that inequality breeds resentment.

The boys in the family led an even more rough and tumble existence than the girls. My brothers recall being thrown in the river at a young age to learn to swim. At other times they'd fill toesacks with empty jars to help them stay afloat. Big Hoke also remembers the little boy's delight at lighting matches and starting grass fires. On one occasion, he accidently burnt down an entire field, which he staunchly denied when apprehended by his elders. Another time, while chopping wood, Little Hoke cut half of his foot off with an axe and nearly bled to death. Aunt Ann, who was visiting at the time, sent Big Hoke running for help to a faith healer about a mile away. This woman had the gift of healing at a distance. Taking down her big Bible, she read a verse about the Lord's power of healing and commanded the bleeding to stop. To everyone's astonishment, it did, and Little Hoke survived.

Family Tragedy

Such miracles were the exception rather than the rule. In January 1940, Essie, my mother's twin sister, couldn't get to a doctor and died of pneumonia. Earlier she had suffered a miscarriage. She was thirty-eight. The two sisters had been inseparable, and her loss came as a big shock. About six months later, our family's greatest tragedy occurred.

One evening Daddy was playing poker in town with Uncle Claude and a Cherokee Indian. They were playing in a small eating establishment in Muse. It contained a restaurant—"a greasy spoon," according to one of my brothers—and a dance floor. Whiskey was sold under the counter in the back room. Uncle Claude had borrowed money to enter the poker game. As he won, Claude was paying it back to some other men watching from the sidelines. The Indian didn't like the money leaving the game and started to fight with my uncle. Then Dad, as Claude's older brother, took up the fight. The town constable arrived to stop the argument. He put my father out one door and the Indian out the other. However, the Indian broke free, circled back and waited for Dad to pass. According

to Laura, Uncle Claude's daughter, Claude saw him and
shouted for Dad to watch out but Daddy wasn't afraid. When
he passed, he was struck hard on the side of the head with a
rock.

After being hit, Father was taken to see a doctor in Pine
Valley, a small sawmill town about twenty-five miles away.
He was still conscious and joked and kidded the whole time,
minimizing his injury in comparison to closer calls he had
experienced in the Argonne Forest in France during the war.
The doctor sent him home to recover from his wound. But
during the night a blood clot formed on the brain, and he died
about 4 A.M. Dot remembers that she couldn't sleep all night
and had a premonition of disaster. At daybreak, she heard Aunt
Margaret in the bedroom whispering, "Poor child, her Daddy's
gone."

Mom told me later that the Indian was to be tried for
murder. After the attack, Uncle Claude took a knife to the
Indian, opening up his intestines, and was arrested. The
Indian's attorney and the prosecuting attorney were brothers.
At the trial in Poteau, the seat of LeFlore County, a deal was
struck whereby the Indian was freed in return for dropping
charges against Uncle Claude.

For many years I did not know many details of my father's
death. The incident seemed shrouded in mystery and when I
would ask about Daddy, there was little anyone could say.
There was only one picture of my Dad that anyone knew about
and none of him with the family. I always wondered what he
looked like and what kind of person he was. Over forty years
later, in preparation of this book, I heard my brothers and
cousins talk in detail about the incident for the first time. Bill
said that the Indian had killed two men previously while
migrating around the country, working at logging and odd
jobs.

"I was thirteen or fourteen at the time," Bill recalled.
"There was a lot of drinking, gambling, and killing going on.

Another man in town, Buster Kress, was killed in a crap game over ten cents."

I asked Bill if he knew the Indian's name.

"I'll never forget it," he replied solemnly as if the tragedy had happened only yesterday. "It was Frank Kino."

Big Hoke told me that the Indian himself was later killed under mysterious circumstances. Rumor had it that kinfolk of one of the men he had killed finally caught up with him in the mountains and administered "frontier justice."

As a child, I often asked my brothers and sisters, "Do you remember Daddy? What was he like?"

Then, as if searching for some bit of information that would ease my mind, they would begin: "Well, he was a good farmer. He could grow crops when no one else in the valley could.

"He was a natural-born hunter and fisherman. Venison, wild hogs, ducks, geese, squirrel, turkeys, rabbits, and fish. He was a good provider for his family.

"He had a sense of humor. Everyone liked him. He hadn't an enemy in the world."

"No one messed with him. The Fields had a reputation for being tough."

"More people came to his funeral than came to the big annual Fourth of July barbeque. Everybody in the county came to pay their respects."

Then from Mother I heard, "You were a daddy's girl. The first word you ever said was 'Daddy' and you didn't say anything else for a long time. And you used to follow him around and hang on to his knee. Then when he died, you'd go to the window and watch and wait for him to come home."

There were funny stories, too. Like the time Father bought a brand new Model-A or Model-T car when they first came out (I never could remember which) and ran it into a tree on the way home.

These stories portrayed Daddy as a man with a strong spirit and one who cared for his family. So they would ease my mind for awhile. But then when our family would get together I'd think of him again and ask, "How did he die?" And once again I'd hear the story of how he and my uncle had been in a poker game with an Indian.

2.

And the Cotton is High

If religion was a thing that money could buy,
Coming for to carry me home,
The rich would live and the po' would die,
Coming for to carry me home.

AFTER DADDY'S DEATH, Mother had no income and took in washing and ironing and worked in the cotton fields. One year she made enough money to buy a milk cow. But she could not stop thinking about Daddy or the way he died.

For generations, women on the frontier had experienced great physical hardship and emotional turmoil after the death of spouses, children, or other loved ones. Many sank into despair or madness, while others soothed their pain with alcohol or opium-laced patent medicines. Mother was strong and determined not to suffer such a fate.

Mother's own people all lived in Texas, and it was only natural that after being widowed she join them and seek a fresh start. She sold the cow to get enough money to move, and in 1943 we left Muse and moved to a farm on the outskirts of Munday, a sleepy country town in the North Texas plains where her brother, Henry, lived.

I was four years old when we left Oklahoma. For a ways, we traveled down U.S. 271, the ending of the old Trail of Tears which the Cherokees, Creeks, and other Eastern Indians had been forcibly removed from their homelands a century earlier. The memories of the trek are vague—some may have been from stories told around the dinner table, others from actual recall. We came to Texas in an old cattle truck with slats on the side and a tarp over part of it. My brothers rode in the back—the twins, Little Hoke and Big Hoke, and M.J.—and my oldest brother Bill who was in charge of everything. I think I spent most of the four-hundred-fifty-mile ride in the cab with Mother and two men who'd been hired to help with the journey. There was simply no room for the family dog, Did-he-bite-you, as much as he wanted to come. When we pulled out of Muse, he chased the truck as hard as he could until it disappeared from sight.

When we first got to Texas we stayed with my mother's uncle, Henry Thompson, and his wife, Ada. They lived on a small farm near Munday. They had a few farm animals and an old tractor seat out in the back that we played on a lot. Sometimes we picked corn from the garden, cut it off the cob, and made sweet corn. Sometimes we boiled it. It was very sweet and delicious. That was a very pleasant time of my life, playing outdoors and being around other people.

Once I was running around the house chasing the twins and saw a snake going up the side of the house. I was so scared. The boys had gone inside when they passed the back entrance, but I was still running around looking for them. Ada was especially fond of the twins, to the extent I felt left out. She would put some money on the dresser in her room, and then when they didn't take it, she would make such a big fuss about how honest they were. I suppose it was her way of teaching them to be honest. But she never tried that with me. Maybe she knew intuitively that I would've considered it dishonest not to take it when she had so much and I had so little.

We didn't stay on the farm long, though. We moved into town into an imitation brick house. There I began to meet relatives on my mother's side. I especially remember my Aunt Gussie's daughter's visiting. They sat beside me on the sofa and bragged about some of my school work. I was so surprised. My feelings about myself began to improve.

For a while, we worked in the cotton fields to help Mother

make a living. She was a hard worker, and one of my most enduring memories of her is pulling the long, canvas bags down the rows filling them with cotton boles as she'd go. Then when she'd weigh in, her load would usually total over one hundred pounds. And that was when she was over forty years old and had had six children. She was only about 5'2" tall so she didn't appear as strong as she actually was. I've since learned that height and strength are not synonymous.

Since I was the littlest and too small for a sack of my own, I used to leave the cotton I pulled in little piles in the middle of the rows for Mom to pick up. This led to the discovery of centipedes. One day I came upon a little creature with so many legs crawling on the ground and was told it was a centipede. At other times I roamed the fields with my young cousin looking for butterflies. Since I was very young, not as much was expected of me, and I enjoyed playing in the fields while they worked.

Later Mother went to work at a laundry. The building had a lot of steam pipes overhead and low to the floor at foot level. It was scary because you never knew when the hot steam might start pouring out, but I always begged to go to the laundry with her. She worked hard all day long washing on machines that had wringers on them and hanging the clothes in the sun to dry. Then she'd spend long hours ironing at the ironing board. She made many friends and enjoyed visiting as she worked. She rarely complained.

In spite of our limited income, we were able to travel some. Mother loved to travel and visit friends and relatives—both nearby and far away. I recall sitting on the porch swing for what seemed to me an eternity as she visited with our neighbors, the Prices, and later going inside for a venison sandwich. When we travelled out of the city, it was by bus or train or in someone else's car as Mother never drove or owned a car in her life. She would go all the way across the country to visit one of her children (with the rest of her brood in hand), and she might stay for several weeks, or even a month, if there was a new grandchild. I can remember riding on street cars, having my picture taken with large groups of people who were in some manner related to us—and experiencing the gala atmosphere of open air markets where people bargained over the prices of sequined felt jackets, straw purses, and other items unique to that area. Once we went from Texas to Washington State. We looked out from the bus windows at snow-covered mountains and deep chasms and wondered if we'd ever make it back to flat land. At one of the bus stops, they had slot machines that you put a coin in. If the same pictures came up across the top (all apples or all lemons, for example), you won. A stranger gave me a dime, and I played the slot machine and won some money. I was elated as I rushed back to the bus to show what I'd won. But Mom didn't share my excitement because she considered this gambling and naturally didn't want me to have any part of it. Later, when in her sixties, one of her children persuaded her to take a plane trip, and she really appreciated it, having travelled by all the slower methods.

In Texas, as in Oklahoma, Mother loved to cook for her children and relatives. We didn't have much fresh meat, except on Sundays or holidays when we would have beef, chicken, or turkey with gravy and all the trimmings. Usually we had cheap canned meat or canned tuna or salmon, which she added in small volume to cornmeal and made into patties or croquettes. Growing up we didn't have much dairy food either. Our neighbors, the Smiths, would give us fresh milk from time to time, and the cool, white liquid was such a treat. We called regular raw milk "sweet milk" to distinguish it from clabbered milk—a sour milk—and buttermilk. On special occasions, we would have Longhorn cheese in round chunks. Aside from the expense, we didn't have a refrigerator to store it, only an icebox. The icebox had to be constantly refilled with new ice, which came in big chunks and had to be chopped with an ice pick. Eggs were more plentiful, and I especially liked them deviled. Later on when we could afford it, we had milk and dairy food more often. Mother thought, as most mothers

did then, that milk and other dairy food were very good for
our health.

Though we didn't have much fresh animal food, Mother
used animal fat liberally in cooking. One of my earliest memories in Munday is of her making cracklings from a butchered
hog. Cracklings are the solid part of the fat that remains when
the lard is rendered out. Mother used cracklings to make cornbread. It was oily, greasy, and had a rich taste, and we loved it.
Cracklings could also be used to make lye soap, and I remember
she and Aunt Ada would build a fire outdoors under a big
black pot and boil the fat with water and lye. The mixture
would be stirred until the cracklings dissolved and turned
creamy white. Then it would harden, be cut into small cubes,
and stored for use in washing dishes or clothes.

In the kitchen, Mother would also spend hours making
homemade rolls and biscuits. She would knead them and let
them rise and knead them and let them rise. By the time they
were baking in the oven, everyone was drooling. We didn't
have store-bought bread and baked goods as much as people
do now. We didn't quite trust them. They were OK to use in
a pinch but not for daily fare.

Store-bought sweets also were not in our budget. For
ordinary desserts we'd have biscuits with chocolate gravy,
molasses, or corn syrup. On holidays, Mother would make a
pecan or mince meat pie and baked or candied sweet potatoes,
and she was always trying out a new homemade cake recipe.
Sometimes too we'd have homemade preserves. My favorite
was peach. I liked to eat them fresh from the tree too, but you
paid a heavy price if they were a little green. The twins and
I suffered many a stomachache from eating them before they
were fully ripe. In summer, we also enjoyed fresh watermelon.
We grew our own one year and would go into the melon
patch, bust one open, and eat the heart out of it right on the
spot. Other than bananas, which were cheap, we didn't have
much fresh fruit. On Christmas we would receive apples or
oranges as a gift and always considered them a special treat.

By the time I was ten or eleven, I used to walk the half mile to the store for Mom and buy groceries for her. Once I bought some date rolls with pecans and jelly in them and ate them all myself. They were so delicious. But the next time Mom was in the store, the clerk told her what I'd been buying. She knew such luxuries were not our custom, and I was reprimanded.

Vegetables came primarily from the garden, especially potatoes, tomatoes, turnip greens, green beans, and okra. The closest thing to a pickle we had was chow-chow. Made from tomato, onions, and cucumbers that had been seasoned with vinegar, sugar, and other seasonings, it was customarily aged by hanging upside down in a cloth sack overnight. Chow-chow was a traditional frontier delicacy. Then sometimes in the summer, Mom would marinate cucumbers in vinegar and salt, and we found those very refreshing.

Considering how hard she worked at the laundry, Mother cooked a lot at home. The oilcloth on the table around which we ate always had a sheen that reflected its use, but she was quick to replace it if it began to look too worn. And she always had a supply of tableclothes for Sunday dinners and other special occasions. We ate out rarely. Occasionally on Sunday when my brothers were doing something else, she would take me out to a local restaurant.

Although she went only to about the eighth grade in school, Mother valued education. Seldom a day went by that she wasn't reading something. She liked to read *True Romances* and magazines like that. I guess it added new dimensions to her own life. And she always encouraged me to go to college, to get my degree. Even years later after I'd had a year of college and dropped out, I remember her writing (she always wrote about once a week) and saying, "Why don't you save your pennies and go back to school?"

She was very handy with a needle and thread. She once crocheted a full-size ecru-colored bedspread. It took her years to complete it. Then she sold it at one of the local dry good stores for fifty dollars to buy food, clothing, and Christmas gifts for us. She also crocheted many doilies and things for the home and for family and friends, giving away more than she kept. She also enjoyed quilting and was always making a quilt top for one of the children or grandchildren. She pieced the quilts by hand. Sometimes I'd come home from school and find her putting up a quilt frame. It consisted of four pieces of wood that hung down from the ceiling on string and were clamped together at the four corners. Then women there would ask me to pull up a chair and help them. My stitches were by far the largest ones in the quilt, but they were never taken out and redone. They went right in there with the neat small ones.

Mother always kept herself neat and clean and preferred simple cotton dresses and practical shoes with a medium or low heel and seldom wore any jewelry next to the skin. She preferred a brooch or pin that could be worn on a dress or coat.

She was frugal and managed our limited income well. She was extended credit by the local merchants but used it only to replace some item like a refrigerator or sofa but never for luxury items such as a television or record player. Sometimes one of us would help her pay it out, but she never depended on us for things. All of the children at one time or another helped Mom pay the bills and get other things she needed, but she always assumed responsibility for paying a debt.

While she never had much money, she tried not to worry us about her finances. Once in a while if the twins or I asked for spending money, she'd say, "You can't get blood out of a turnip," and we knew that meant she didn't have any to spare. If she had some money, she shared it. If she needed some, she earned it, and if she borrowed it, she paid it back—even if it took her years to do it.

We always slept with the windows open (during the warm season) and used to go to bed at night with just the screen latched on the door. She was so trusting and yet she never suffered harm from this practice. And if a thief had come, they would've been more inclined to leave something to fill the house instead of take something away.

The only thing I objected to in Mother's personal habits was that she used to dip snuff. Snuff is finely ground tobacco that has been seasoned. Some has a sweet flavor. Wm. Garrett was her favorite brand. She kept an old can in which she would crumble up paper to be used as her "spit can." "Barbara," she would say to me, "Bring me my spit can." This was a most distasteful task to me. And the snuff turned her teeth dark. No one I knew of dipped snuff, and for a long time I was embarrassed to bring my friends home.

Through it all, the good times and the bad times, Mother had a good sense of humor. She seldom complained in spite of all her problems, and she wasn't one to feel sorry for herself. She would hum as she worked. Though her children were always a primary concern, she seemed to make friends wherever she went. People were always coming to "Aunt Dessie's" for a cup of coffee or to see if she needed anything from the store. Then after the grandchildren started calling her "Ma," other friends and relatives and neighbors picked up on it, and she became "Ma" to all of them.

Days of Infamy

War broke out in the Pacific in December, 1941, and it was not long before my oldest brother, Bill, was inducted in the army. He had left the Oklahoma hills at age fifteen, about a year after Dad died. Wandering around, he stayed with relatives in Oklahoma City and worked at the Nabisco Company. Then he followed the wheat harvest before returning to Muse and helping us move to Texas.

I was too young to understand the far off war and thought Bill was just flying around having a good time. When Mom wrote him, she'd ask me what I wanted to say to him and put that in her letter. At other times, I'd write out my own letter to send to him along with hers. This would be in a form of scribbling, but the thoughts were there. Bill always had a few words for me in his letters. We really looked forward to his

correspondence. This started a pattern of letter writing,
learned like so many other things at my mother's side, that
continued throughout my life.

I really missed Bill and couldn't wait for him to come home.
He was handsome and looked terrific in his uniform. On leave,
he would carry me around on his shoulders and bring me pretty
clothes and gifts. Once he took me to the drug store to get an
ice cream cone, and I cried because it was chocolate. I didn't
like chocolate. He said, "Well, what kind did you want?" And
I said, "Vanilla." The next time he'd get me vanilla. But it
wasn't just the ice cream that endeared me to him. He had a
way of making people happy. We always laughed a lot when
he was home and got to go different places and do different
things.

Soon Bill's unit received orders, and he left for the Far East.
I never knew Mother's thoughts about the Far East, but my
thoughts were clear. One of our neighbors used to talk about
the Japanese to me and tell me how they tortured captured
Americans and her final conclusion was, "They're not human!"
She also said they had slanted eyes and were "yellow," and
I thought this meant their skin was yellow. I didn't associate
it with the psychological stereotypes of the time. Feelings run
high when your children are halfway around the world fighting
and your knowledge of world affairs is shaped by radio and
newspapers.

Mother used to bake fruit cakes to send to Bill when he went
overseas. She would make a big pan full of batter that would
make several cakes. Then she'd use rum to preserve them once
baked and mail them to him along with cookies. M.J. and the
twins were in school at that time so I had more time alone
with Mom.

My sister, Dot, spent some time with us in Munday, too.
After finishing high school in Muse, she went to work at a
tuberculosis sanitarium in Talihina. The hospital had a dairy
and served milk to all the patients. The odor was so overwhelming that for the rest of her life she couldn't drink it.

While a freshman in high school, Dot had begun dating Orville Fisher, a senior from Big Cedar, who joined the service after graduation. Following the attack on Pearl Harbor, the young couple's plans to postpone marriage changed, and they eloped. They moved around the country every six to nine months until Orville's unit was sent to England in 1944.

From Alabama, where her husband had last been stationed, Dot drove back to Texas to live with us at Mother's. On Christmas Eve, she received a telegram that Orville's troop ship had been torpedoed and sunk on a crossing to France. Everyone aboard was missing.

Orville never returned from the war. Dot and her daughter, Cheryl, who was born the following spring, lived with us or nearby for several years.

Life in Munday

Munday was a typical North Texas farming community that had sprung up at the turn of the century. The red sandy loam soil could grow almost anything provided it was irrigated. At one time or another, Munday was known as the hog capital, the poultry capital, and the vegetable capital of the region. The old timers classified the seasons in Knox County as winter, sand-storm time, summer, and autumn. Windy in spring and hot in summer, the area could be surprisingly cold in winter. Blizzards swept in from the snowy peaks of Colorado, bringing sleet and snow and cold spells that could last for weeks.

There were also sporadic tornadoes. On a number of occasions when the sky darkened, Mom would be outside watching along with the neighbors. Then would come a strong warning, "Let's get to the cellar." Sometimes it was in our back yard, but more often we took refuge in a neighbor's storm shelter. We would pull the weathered door back until the hinges creaked and then descend the steps with a kerosene lamp to illuminate the darkness. The last one in, always one of the grown-ups, would close the door behind him. We would

huddle together on wooden benches, with a musty smell filling
our nostrils and the damp earthen walls chilling our bones,
until the storm had passed. It felt like being in prison, and
I was always jubilant when the doors were opened and I could
see the sky again.

Munday's early history was dominated by Parson Hanks, an
itinerant Methodist preacher. By the turn of the century two
towns had sprung up, separated by about a thousand yards of
prairie. Each vied for lucrative railroad rights. When Parson
Hanks arrived, he was convinced that the two halves of town
should not remain apart and decided to construct a church
midway between them. When he staked out a building, it
turned out to be slightly closer to the east town, so the west
folks "kicked" and he suspended construction.

Meanwhile, a severe drought came, blowing hot wind and
sand for more than a month. Parson Hanks bought a tabernacle
—a large moveable prayer tent—and held nightly revivals.
They were a great success, and after he had converted most of
the townspeople he chose the east town to build his church.
But a rival denomination made plans to build in the west
town, and he perceived the division would continue. Finally, he
went to the people of the east town and got them to donate
land to people in the west town. Two railroad engines were
brought in and put to work pulling houses from west to east.
The houses were moved by putting long skids underneath and
then with strong cables fastening them to an engine and
from two to four horse-drawn wagons on a side and pulling
together. "In one month's time there was one town instead
of two," Parson Hanks wrote in his memoirs, "and with but
little exception, a good spirit and a good brotherly feeling
prevailed."

Munday's homes and buildings were made primarily of
wood or sheet iron and included a post office, library, newspaper, department and dry good stores, cafes, and drug
stores. The drug stores contained the usual pharmaceutical
section they have today, plus stationery items, greeting cards,

make-up, and jewelry, as well as a full-service soda fountain. People would stop in when they came to town and get a cheese sandwich or tuna or chicken salad or perhaps an ice cream sundae or chocolate milkshake or Coca Cola or coffee. In the 1920s, the great White Way was installed—a series of fourteen electric lights in the center of Main Street and cross streets leading off Main. However, so many automobiles backed into the lights or hit them while being driven along the street that the White Way lights were "torn out by their roots" and new mercury-vapor lights installed in the 1940s when I was a child.

Sometimes medicine shows would come to town, and we'd go out and sample the wares, including linaments guaranteed to relieve tired muscles, salves for burns, insect bites, and any number of other maladies and patent medicines. For itching, people used sulfur and terpentine rubbed on the outside. For laxatives, cat's draw or black drought were common. My sister recalls us using poultices and hot towels and drinking herbs and sassafras tea for common ailments. My constitution was generally strong, and I had few childhood illnesses, mostly measles and sore throats. In Oklahoma, we lived twenty-five miles from the nearest doctor. As a baby, I had pneumonia and was given whiskey to get well. In Munday, the major health problem I had was called "pink eye." I'd wake up with my eyes swollen shut and the eyelids stuck together. Not being able to see was a scary feeling. Mom would bathe them with warm salt water, and they'd usually open.

After about a year we moved to a house near the railroad tracks. It had cloth hanging between the rooms for privacy as there were no doors between the bedrooms and living room. There was a kerosene stove in the kitchen along with a round oak dining table. There was a coal burning stove and buckets of coal lined the wall in the living room. My brother, Leborn, was supposed to get up and start the fire, but he was a slow mover in the morning and once burned his hands badly. Mom was always yelling at him and Cleburn to try to get them to hurry and get ready. I realize now that a man's energy comes up slowly and they tend to be more active at night while women are more alert and active in the morning. I should have been building the fire!

Grandmother Thompson came and stayed with us for awhile. I was told not to tell the welfare worker that she was visiting. I guess that affected how much help the family could receive. But I was so excited about seeing the welfare worker when I got home from school that day that I forgot and, sure enough, the first thing I told her was about my grandma coming to visit.

My grandmother burned herself severely while living with us. She spilled scalding water on the front of her legs. Her legs were very fat at the time, and the whole front of one of them was covered with blisters. It looked awful and the pain was severe. She and Mom put some salve on it, but that turned out to be the wrong thing to do as the doctor had to remove the salve before he bandaged it. Looking back, I'm not sure whether it was the wrong thing to have applied the salve or to have called the doctor. But Grandma Thompson had a strong constitution, and her leg eventually healed. The memory of it lingered a long time.

It was in this house that my brother M.J. got polio. Earlier, in Muse he had contracted typhoid fever. The doctor used to come to the house and make him get out of bed and try to stand and move his arms and legs. He was frightfully thin. It had been very hot that summer, and we drank a lot of tea and ate a lot of watermelon and other fruit and sweets. We didn't have air conditioning either. I don't even recall a fan. At that time, polio was considered contagious and no connection was made to diet. So a big sign went up on the front door: "Quarantined." We were told that no one could visit us, nor could we go out until M.J. was better. All of his clothes had to be kept separate from the rest of the family's, and we were not to touch them. I felt so sorry for him as I watched him try to

stand and move his legs. And we all felt like lepers, wondering
why things like crippling diseases happened to people.

When M.J. was better, my Aunt Lucy came to see us and
brought eight or nine dresses that she had made for me. I
thought I was in heaven having so many dresses. We didn't
have any closets, but we hung them on a cord across the corner
of the room. My mother would also have a friend of hers make
a dress for me from time to time when she was able. Then one
Easter three women gave me dresses to wear to church. They
were all pink. One was pink and white striped with a sash
that tied in the back. All of the dresses were beautiful, but
I didn't know which one to wear to keep from offending the
women who gave me the others, so I just stayed home!

The Second World War was now over. Thankfully, my
brother Bill had survived. On a troop ship to the Philippines, he
he had a vivid dream which convinced him he would return in
one piece. He dreamed of coming home after the war and
telling people about a big battle at Lynagen Gulf. At the time,
no one aboard the ship had ever heard of Lynagen Gulf, but it
proved to be one of the turning points in the war. After losing
the Philippines, it was only a matter of time before Japan was
defeated and the long war in the Pacific came to an end. The
dream gave Bill confidence in a higher, spiritual reality and in
his own intuition. He lost many soldier friends in the heavy
shelling and came back with heart-rending and hair-raising
tales. He received a Purple Heart, but he was never one to
show it off.

One Christmas Bill came to Munday to visit us. It was a
very special occasion. He'd married a girl named Bertha, and
they went shopping for everyone. They got me a little make-up
kit, which made me feel so grown up, and a gold bracelet—the
first piece of jewelry I ever owned. Sometimes part of our
Christmas was supplied by Goodfellows and other groups that
gave gifts to the poor. Once, searching through a big box of
toys they'd left with us, I found a wrist watch—a real Mickey
Mouse wrist watch! The twins had been busy with other toys

and were disappointed that they hadn't found it. I treasured it and often wondered who had given it.

Mother always swept the floors and tried to keep the house neat. She got upset a lot with my brothers and used to use a small switch with which to spank them. Once she got mad at them and sent me to get a switch. When I came back, she said, "That's not a switch, it's a tree limb." I really thought I was helping her shape them up.

We didn't have candy very often in those days. Once Mother got a box of chocolate-covered creams for Christmas. She put them in the bottom drawer of a dresser, and we always asked permission before taking a piece. I remember once too we had nothing for breakfast but a can of pineapple. We sat at the table, and each one was served a slice on a plate and offered a prayer of thanks for it.

We had running water at this house but still used an outdoor toilet and bathed in metal tubs. Our cousins visited a lot but were quite a bit older than I was and didn't always want me around. Sometimes, when I was lonely, I had imaginary playmates. I would get a branch from a tree and put my arm around it, and we strolled up and down the yard, talking all the while. We used to pick up twigs that had fallen from the trees, and with tin cans and rocks and whatever we could find build filling stations, houses, and roads in the dirt in the front yard.

My aunt Etta, Evelyn's mother, told me to come by before school, and she used to wash my legs and comb my hair as Mom would already be at work. Usually we walked to school, but sometimes I'd ride to school with a girl called Gayle Littlefield. She always had such beautiful clothes and was naturally very pretty. I felt jealous in a way, especially since we had the same name. But I couldn't understand why her mother still dressed her. I'd been dressing myself for years and tying my shoes since I was six.

It was while living in this house that I came to understand that we were poor. In Oklahoma, many friends and family had about the same standard of living. But now I compared our little house to the spacious ones around me with their lovely furnishings and gardens. One day as I walked home across the grassy knoll, I noticed how very tiny it was compared to theirs and that the paint had long ago worn thin. There wasn't any grass in the yard, and the little step that you stepped up on to go inside had never been secured. About that time, the mother of one of my classmates told her that she couldn't play with me because I lived "across the railroad tracks." But Mom had just told me I couldn't play with her because she "cussed," and she didn't want me to pick up that habit.

When I was old enough, I was sent off to school. For a long time we didn't have any books to read. I kept asking the teacher, "When are we going to get our books?" When we received them, I learned to read quickly and soon was in the top group in the class. School came to be an important part of my life. I remember we had a school play, and I was playing a baby. I dressed in white and just sang my heart out. At the end of my first year in school (during the eighth grade graduation exercises), my friend Gerald and I had our names called out as having the highest grades in the class. We were asked to come forward to get the award, but Mother held me back because she wasn't sure it was me, as they hadn't used my full name "Barbara Gale" but only said "Barbara Fields." But the teacher noticed and later brought the award by the house. It was my very first book—*A Child's Garden of Verses*—and I treasured it for many years.

The Wrong Side of the Tracks

While living in this little house on the wrong side of the tracks, I came to know my relatives, the Fords. There were Uncle Ray and Aunt Etta. Ray worked at the utility company, and the company provided a house next door to where he worked. It seemed an ideal arrangement. Uncle Ray and Aunt Etta had

several children. Mozelle was the oldest, followed by Ray
Darrel, Jesse, Evelyn, and Bobby.

There were some happy times in my life associated with this
family as well as unhappy ones. I remember we used to play
hopscotch on the sidewalk and a game called "May I." The
object of this game was for one of the players to move to the
other end and become the leader. Some children would line up
at one end, and a leader would stand at the other end and call
the person's name and give a command such as "Bobby, take
three giant steps." Bobby had to say "May I?" before he
proceeded. He could take steps, jumps, hops, and skips forward
or backward or sideways. I enjoyed the activity and being a
part of the group.

Another game we played was called "Red Rover." Children
formed two lines facing each other a fair number of yards apart.
Then they would hold hands or clasp each other's arms and
say, "Red Rover, Red Rover, let Evelyn come over." Then
Evelyn would leave the line she was in and try to break
through the other line. If she did, she took a person back with
her to her own line so it got bigger. If she didn't, she stayed
with their line. Naturally being the youngest and the smallest,
it was hard for me to break through the line, so I was one of
the last to be chosen. I hated that.

While competitive games like this had value in giving us
exercise, they instilled within us that strong and big and tough
are better—qualities that Texans of all ages had long come to
admire. They also taught us to compete with rather than
cooperate with one another.

One of my favorite pastimes with Uncle Ray and Aunt Etta
was sitting outside, looking at the night sky, and trying to
find the Big Dipper, the Little Dipper, and other constellations.
I loved just looking at the stars. Sometimes we'd sit on the
porch instead. That was pleasant, too, in addition to helping
Etta dig up the front flower bed and plant flowers.

We'd also draw with chalk on the sidewalk and play hopscotch and see who could spell the best. Once Jesse decided he was going to plant cotton and he did. It was wonderful watching something grow from small seeds.

Then sometimes Bobby and I had spelling matches just between the two of us. He always decided who had spelled the word correctly because he was two years older than me. I don't know how much this game did for my spelling, but it taught me something more important—respect for my elders.

Years later, when any of the Fords visited Pecos, Texas, where Mom was then living, they would always come to Aunt Dessie's (Mom's) to eat. I thought they were imposing and would tell Mom, "I wouldn't cook for all of them." But she had a different view. Once they were there I was glad, and Mom didn't seem to mind the extra work, and she did set a good table. So while it was never said to me in so many words, I learned that people become families and stay together by eating together.

The Yellow House

From the white house in Munday, we moved to the yellow house. It was much larger and nicer. We still had an outdoor toilet that was a good half-block walk away, but we had a living room, two bedrooms, and a kitchen. I must have been about eight or nine at the time.

My sister Dot had remarried by this time. Her husband, Bob Barton, had been born and raised in Munday and had just come back from the war. He was a veteran of the Bataan Death March. From a prisoner-of-war camp in the Philippines, he and a group of captured American and British soldiers had been taken to a forced labor camp in Japan. There he worked in a shipyard in Onomichi. To supplement their meager rations, the men stole white rice, sugar, daikon, miso, tofu, and other foods from their captors, and when they were caught they were tortured. One day a guard told Bob about a tremendous bomb that had been exploded over Hiroshima, sixty miles to the west. Shortly after, the Japanese abandoned the camp, the war ended, and the surviving POWs were liberated.

Bob and Dot met in the local drug store where she started working. After the death of her first husband, she received some money which she used to buy a small house. Bob worked at a cotton gin, and together with my niece, Cheryl, and their new son, Scotty, they often came by to visit. Dot also helped me with clothes, especially at Easter when she would buy me a new outfit every year. She and Bob had a nice small house, and I would go by on my way home from school and help wash Scotty's diapers and help around the house and earn some spending money. I loved to visit them because their house was so nicely decorated and also because she always had some delicous food cooked—including nice desserts like pecan pie or cookies. And they had Coca-Colas. These were so delicious and such a treat. She was always creating order in the house, and she has always been an excellent cook by modern standards. I was fortunate to grow up around women who loved to cook for their families.

Bill and Bertha occasionally visited with their young son, James. Bertha was pregnant with Robert at this time. She had only three dresses, but she always laundered them, ironed them, and looked fresh and crisp. I never remember her complaining.

The twins were into a lot of mischief at this time. They would pretend they were in bed, then get up, and slip off down to the cotton gin and play in the piled up residue. Farmers from miles around would bring in their cotton in big trailers to be mechanically processed. The tightly compacted hulls piled up outside the suction machines, and kids loved to play in them. It's a wonder they didn't get covered in that stuff and suffocate. My uncle, Tuck Duvall, and his wife, Norene, took them home with them to Oklahoma one summer. They thought they would be helping Mom by taking them off her hands while she was recuperating from surgery. The boys stayed four to six weeks and ran off and hitchhiked home by themselves. They were only about fourteen. Their bond to home and family was very strong.

Big and Little Hoke were also into automobiles. They got a Model A or T from somewhere and painted it yellow and black and tried to fix it up. Then there was another car they were working on in the front yard. Once I climbed into the front seat while they were fixing it up underneath, and the car fell on one of my brothers. I don't know if I had anything to do with it falling or not. But the other brother practically lifted the car off his twin by himself.

My brothers were always fighting with each other, but if they were challenged by someone outside the family they closed ranks. In her memoirs about growing up in Munday a generation before I did, Lorena Wilson Mahan described the futile efforts of a gentlemanly school superintendent to discipline the youngsters of her day including my brother-in-law's family, the Bartons:

> There were always fights on and off the school grounds. Under Mr. Routh's tenure, there were more and bigger ones, because he was such a determined crusader in his efforts to quell the riots. Blonde hair blowing, coat-tails flying, he would dash frantically to the scene of action, quite powerless to do anything about it, except to "accidently" get pushed around a bit. Sometimes these melees were staged for just his benefit, but usually because there simply was not sufficient outlet for the excess energies of these strong, strapping, overgrown boys.

Perhaps, as Mrs. Mahan further noted, there was "too much difference in their age span to make for effective group tactics." But it was all in good fun. Invariably, as she noted, the young men of the town developed "a strong sense of integrity and all turned out to be God-fearing, law-abiding citizens."

My extracurricular interests ran in a more cultural and artistic direction. Once in third or fourth grade, our class celebrated Halloween with a square dance. My sister made a beautiful light pink skirt, which opened into a full circle, and had a tie belt with a big pink bow in back. The little boys in class were decked out in plaid shirts and clean jeans. Our teacher served as caller, and we practiced to the music of old 78 rpm records. The square dance was the hit of the school carnival. On the dance floor, doing allemande rights and lefts, arches, Texas stars, and promenades, I felt right at home.

3.

The Streets are Paved with Gold

Promenade two and promenade four
Keep that calico off of the floor.

NEXT TO MY FAMILY AND ENVIRONMENT, the church had
the biggest influence in shaping my early life.
Munday's population was about fifteen hundred. The
whole town could be divided into two groups—those who
went to church and those who didn't. The vast majority
belonged to the first group. Those in the second group were
automatically looked upon as "wicked" regardless of what
else they did. In general, the people who didn't go to church
were more attracted to dancing, partying, and fooling around
with the opposite sex so they automatically reinforced the
townfolk's opinion of them.

While growing up in Munday, I attended several different
churches with my friends. But the one I considered my "home
church," and went to almost every Sunday, was the First
Baptist Church.

The basic religious principle of the Southern Baptist church
was that we were born in sin and alienated from God. In
other words, God and man are two. Inherent in the teachings
is that man is not able to save himself partly because of
uncontrollable forces or evil desires that we're born with and
partly our self-interest in all matters as opposed to the interest
of family and society.

Sunday after Sunday we read John 3:16 aloud and were
required to memorize it—"For God so loved the world that
he sent his only begotten Son, that whosoever believeth in
Him should not perish but have everlasting life." To be

considered saved, we had to publicly express our faith that
Jesus had died on the cross to save us from our sins. Then
we were to accept the Bible as God's holy word and the
authority of people in the past who wrote the scriptures.
Little or no emphasis was placed on our own intuition or
judgment or even the teachings of our parents.

Growing up in this atmosphere was a source of both
anxiety and pleasure. A friend's mother, with good intentions
I'm sure, filled us at an early age with stories about hellfire
and damnation. She warned us that if we didn't live according
to the doctrine of the church we would burn in hell when we
died. She gave long discourses about the devil also—how he
was red, had horns, and tended hot fires with his pitchfork.
I spent many troubled hours over the years as a result of
those stories before I understood the fear and ignorance on
which they were based.

There were many injunctions in the Bible that were credible
to me, for example, that we should love and honor our parents
and love our neighbors as ourselves and love all the people
of the world as Jesus did. But other things were difficult for
me to accept such as the story about how Jesus fed the multitude with two small fishes. I came from a frugal family but
that was stretching it a bit. I also found the story about
Jonah being swallowed by a whale and being spit out again
hard to believe. I finally concluded that these were parables
in which Jesus was trying to teach some principle that I hadn't
yet comprehended. I considered this an expression of faith
and came to accept things that I couldn't understand while
I continued to pray, study, and grow spiritually.

One of the things I liked most about going to church was
the singing. Part of the time I sang with the congregation
and part of the time with the choir. The songs we sang
reflected our belief that Jesus was our Savior. He was also an
intermediary between us and God. Few people believed that
we could actually communicate directly with God. We had to
go through his son who died for our sins. Still, a person

could "sin" or lose favor with God by committing acts that
were wrong in His sight (as interpreted by the minister) or
by omitting to do things that were beneficial (such as sharing
your beliefs with others and "leading them to Christ"). Then
the devil was blamed for many misdeeds and temptations
rather than the individual. The problem with this teaching is
that unless you accept responsibility, you are powerless to
change. You can spend a whole lifetime waiting for your life
to improve.

The songbooks were replete with hymns about God's son,
Jesus, on whom our salvation depended—"Living for Jesus,"
"Satisfied with Jesus," "Jesus Lifted Me," "He Lives on
High," "Jesus Is Calling," "Standing on the Promises of
Christ, My King," and "The Nail-Scarred Hand." The refrain
from this last one went:

Have you failed in your plan of your storm-tossed life?
Place your hand in the nail-scarred hand.
Are you weary and worn from your toil and strife?
Place your hand in the nail-scarred hand.

According to Southern Baptist teachings, the way you got
saved was by faith in Jesus. Everyone agreed that heaven had
comfortable mansions and streets paved with gold on which
the saved lived joyfully forever. But there was fundamental
disagreement on how to get there. Some people believed that
once you were saved—converted and baptized—you would go
to heaven regardless of how you acted after that. Others
belived you had to perform good deeds throughout your life
—such as giving money to the church building programs and
missionary work—to avoid damnation and attain eternal life.
It was never clear to me just what I had to do to go to
heaven. The harder I tried to do right, the more trouble I
got into.

At the age of twelve, I accepted Christ as my savior and
set off to restore happiness in myself and among my family

and friends. Ironically, I became very unhappy. First of all, the teachings alienated me from my family. I attended church and they didn't, and I was often asked, "Where's Hoke?" or "Where are your brothers?" Naturally I thought they should be "saved" too. So I'd go home and preach to them. They didn't have to go to church. They had their own little preacher that brought the gospel to them.

I remember one day I told my brother that drinking was wrong and that he needed to stop taking beer or he'd go to hell. Naturally he found this statement offensive and responded, "If you can show me one place in the Bible where it says don't drink, I'll stop. Until then, shut up!"

I did look, but I could never make much sense out of the Bible. The same scripture that meant one thing to me meant the exact opposite to someone else. But I never stopped praying for their "lost souls" either, erroneously assuming that the conflict in our family was their fault. On the way home from school, I'd stop about a block from the house and pray that we might have a happy, peaceful family, trying to do my part in the only way I knew.

I also talked to Mother about salvation, though my approach to her was much more subtle. "Mom, are you a Christian?" I ventured one night as she sat reading.

She looked up from her book and said, "Yes, honey, I am."

"Then why don't you ever go to church?"

I said this to this tireless woman who worked at a laundry for six days a week and cooked and cleaned for her children when she got home and went and bought groceries on Sunday, her one day off, and then came home and worked in the garden and made us quilts and mended our clothes and crocheted doilies for the end tables and embroidered linen for gifts.

But she didn't say, "Well, I'd rather relax," or "I feel out of place among the other women with their diamond rings and fancy hats and furs." She just said, "I guess I should."

I felt awful and I never brought the subject up again.

Later on, when she no longer worked at the laundry, she attended church more regularly than I did and immensely enjoyed the activities and friends she made there. Church provided a wealth of social activities that I enjoyed. I developed new friendships and used to go home with one girl on Sunday afternoons who lived in the country. She had a piano, and we'd sit around it and sing songs for hours. They also had a lot to eat, and sometimes her mother would offer me extra ice cream or cobbler with a glass of milk before I left to go back, knowing that it might be awhile before I had any of these foods again. Then one summer, I attended church camp for three or four days. We shared cabins with other girls and our chaperones and swam or played in the creek in the afternoon and sang gospel songs beside it at night. It was a great adventure.

On Sunday nights, we'd usually eat supper at church, and in good weather there would be picnic lunches. Tables would be set up with more food that I'd seen at one time in my whole life. I always had a good appetite and gorged myself on tuna fish salad and pimiento cheese sandwiches, fried chicken, potato and macaroni salads, beans, vegetables and berry and fruit pies.

In addition to the choir, I studied for the girls' auxiliary at the church and graduated from a lady-in-waiting to a queen. In recognition of my achievement, a lady in the church helped me pick out a long dress, and I appeared in a program in a nearby town.

Later, when I was to graduate from the eighth grade, I had no dress to wear. To earn some money, I got a job pulling cotton. My Sunday school teacher heard about it, came to the fields, and asked if she could buy me a dress. I was so relieved. I didn't look forward to the hot cotton fields so much anymore. I didn't realize it took so much work to make so little money. And working wasn't the same without my family. We went to Wichita Falls, a big city about seventy-five miles from Munday, and shopped a long time.

After visiting four or five stores, I picked out the first suit
I ever owned. It had a blue-grey skirt and a matching coat
with a wide collar and was gorgeous. It was very feminine
and yet practical as it could be worn for church, too.

It was about this time that one of the women at the church,
a Mrs. Reeves, wanted to adopt me. Her own daughter had
bled to death following a tonsillectomy. She invited me over
to the house a lot and talked to me about Jesus. I didn't
know at the time what her intentions were. Years later, I
heard about it and that Mother had turned her down.

In addition to usual Sunday services, we often went to
revivals. Some of these were held in large tents that were
pitched in a field and featured visiting preachers with a gift of
oratory or young people aspiring to the ministry. At the
revivals, I was always rededicating my life. I never intentionally did anything wrong. But I always felt I wasn't quite
living up to the ideal so I'd go down the aisle, confess my
faults through tear-filled eyes, and promise the Lord that I
would try again. I guess I really burned a path to the pulpit.

Mother's Illness

We had not been in Munday very long before another tragedy
struck our family. I was about eight or nine when Mother got
sick. I remember her calling a neighbor to the house and
asking her to look at a lump on her breast. I overheard her
say, "Dessie, you'd better go have that seen about." The
next thing I knew Mother had breast cancer and was in surgery in a hospital in nearby Knox City. A lot of family members arrived to help out. My brother Bill and his family came
back to live with us. Grandma Thompson was there and
Logan, Mother's step-brother, who was paralyzed from a car
wreck. My sister Dot came back from Pecos, an old frontier
town about three hundred miles west, where she, Bob, and
their two children had moved.

Mother came home from the hospital bandaged around her

chest. The thing I remember most was the awful smell. The odor around the house was unbearable. The dressings had to be changed daily to absorb the material that oozed from the opening. Also heat lamps were directed toward the area to help it heal. I'd help her unwrap and change the dressings, but the sight of the cavity that existed where her breast was and the smell of the discharging matter was almost too much. The memory of this experience would later help me choose a different path.

The follow-up X-rays indicated some cancer still remained so Mother went back to the hospital a second time and had a radical mastectomy. The surgeon cut the lymph nodes, and she could no longer lift her arm. When she returned home, the skin and tissues were again raw and sore. Mother was never expected to recover, but she did. She survived the cancer, but I think she never got over the treatment for it. I know I never did.

With Mother sick, our home would get incredibly dirty. I did what I could but was not very old. Once again the people in the church assisted us during this crisis. They brought food for the holidays, and I remember how embarrassed I was when once they came and found a can of beer in the icebox—no food, just a can of beer.

When the whole family was home, our diet consisted of bacon or sausage and eggs, biscuits and chocolate gravy, and bologna and cheese sandwiches with lettuce and tomatoes, mayonnaise, mustard, and chips. I was also crazy about peanut butter and used to eat it by the jar. And when there was nothing else to eat, I'd take a piece of white bread and spread it with mustard and then add grease. My brother's complained about that. They had more common sense about eating than I did.

Also, we ate a lot of chicken. Someone gave us some baby chicks. They grew up and multiplied. Mother used to wring the neck off a chicken before cooking it for dinner. This bothered me. She would make chicken and dumplings, fried chicken, and other times serve it with cream gravy. And we had eggs often for breakfast.

Vegetables included candied sweet potatoes, turnip greens, green beans, okra, and two kinds of white potatoes. New potatoes grew in our garden, and I would pull them out of the dirt. Irish potatoes, which were bigger, came from the store, and we enjoyed them fried, mashed, or made into potato salad or potato pancakes.

Then there was roast beef for Sunday dinner and ham when company came and homemade yeasted rolls and homemade cakes. We also enjoyed homemade pies, especially lemon and chocolate with meringue made of sugar and egg whites. But all this changed when my brothers or sister were not around and when Mother was unable to cook. Often we just had cornbread and buttermilk for dinner or a balogna and mayonnaise sandwich.

Eventually Mother got stronger and went back to work at the laundry. And I soon joined her. At the laundry, I would hang out sheets and fold small towels for forty cents an hour. Over the next five years, Mother went to Fort Worth periodically for radium treatments. Right after her surgery, she went for a series, and we stayed with her brother, Jim Jack Thompson, who lived there. The twins, Big and Little Hoke, my brother M.J. and cousin Wayne came along, as well as myself and one of Mother's friends from Munday.

Fort Worth was a long way from home, or so it seemed to me. Next to Wichita Falls, it was the biggest city I had ever been to. My cousins drove me into the city to see the lights, the big department stores windows displaying beautiful clothes, and other goods and appliances. Along with the tall buildings and the mammoth highways filled with shiny new cars and trucks, the sites were mind-boggling and helped divert attention from Mother's sickness.

Coming of Age

After our first trip to Fort Worth, Mother returned for
radiation treatments every so often for her cancer. In the
meantime, I began to suffer tooth problems. I had the first
teeth pulled in my lower jaw. Since no replacements were put
in, the other teeth began to grow at an angle. From then on,
my teeth always felt funny, and I couldn't chew so well.

My self-image at this time started to decline. I felt that
because my lower teeth were not straight, I was unattractive.
One day, I was surprised to overhear a neighbor commenting
to my Mother, "Barbara is getting to be really pretty, isn't
she?" "Well, I don't know. Pretty is as pretty does," my
Mother replied. Evidently I still had some character traits she
didn't approve of, but she never said what they were.

When not at school or involved in social activities at
church, I played with the neighbors, Jacqueline and Margaret
Clowdis. They were much more physically active than I was.
They'd climb up on top of a shed and jump off it or jump
from it to a tree and then climb down. They could never
persuade me to get down this way though I did climb some
of the lower trees at home. We also made a playhouse where
we baked mud pies, served dinner, and nursed our babies.
Then, since we had to buy groceries, we found an empty
shed and filled it with empty cans and bottles, priced them,
set up a change box, and had our own store. And when we
tired of these activities, we'd sit under the tree and read
Nancy Drew mysteries. We used to fight a lot and say we
never wanted to see each other again, but we had so much
fun together when we weren't fighting that we found it easy
to say we were sorry and begin some new venture.

Friday night, I was often allowed to go to the movies with
them. There, as in Fort Worth, I glimpsed a much larger,
more refined world than the hills of Oklahoma or the dusty
Texas plains. These outings were an important part of my
early development. I remember seeing *Gone with the Wind*,

which came out the year I was born, and *The Boy with the Green Hair*. But my favorites were the Western musicals with Gene Autry and Roy Rogers and Dale Evans. I could relate to the happy, cheerful voices of Melody Ranch, the chivalrous way of life that rewarded virtue and honor, and the nostalgia of a time when things were less complicated and carefree. Also, as every girl my age proudly knew, Dale Evans grew up in Uvalde, a small South Texas town just like Munday.

One night, while waiting with Jacqueline and Margaret for their father to pick us up, I left the movie theater to investigate something across the way. When he arrived, he collected his daughters and went home without me. No one in our family had a car or even a telephone so I walked home alone, but I was pretty scared. Then when I got there, Mother was furious, and I received a severe whipping. I'd been whipped many times by now, and I never knew exactly when it might happen or for what reason. Sometimes Leborn or Cleborn would say to Mom, "You never do spank her," and so Mother would spank me, though in my view I hadn't even been around. As a result of these beatings, I began to resent Mother, and I'd protect myself by wearing more clothes when I was going to get a spanking. I found it didn't hurt as much when I had on a dress with a full slip. Also I could bend slightly backward when she struck and escape part of the blow. With all of the mistakes I later made with my son, I have never been one to spank him. Although people are deeply influenced by their early upbringing, they can and do change as the state of their health changes.

Once I was also spanked by a teacher at school for talking in class. He spanked me with a wooden paddle with five holes in it right in front of the whole class. It hurt like the dickens, but I wouldn't give him the pleasure of letting him know. While I fought with the twins, we were united when it came to the outside world. My brothers got upset when they heard what happened and told me, "If he ever tries to do that again, just let us know." I knew they meant it, too.

My brothers were also interested in knives at this time. They were always whittling (carving with wood) and would make pea shooters and things. But they knew how to use them for protection as well. Once, some kids that I rode the school bus with kept bothering me. I took one of my brothers' switchblade knives. On the way home, the kids on the bus taunted me. I took out the knife and flipped it open. One boy cut himself on it. After that they kept their distance, and I was given the name "Slasher." The rest of my classmates were quite surprised that such a mild-mannered young woman came up with such a dangerous knife. It took me a long time to live down that nickname. Finally, because of the freckles that came out when I started working at the laundry and hanging up wash in the bright sun, I was renamed "Spots." It was a great puzzle to me why I suddenly had big freckles all over my face and legs. I tried sitting in a bathtub of cold water and later ordered freckle cream and tried all kinds, but nothing worked. It never occurred to me until years later it was due to my excessive sugar intake and being out in the sun.

The autumn I entered eighth grade, we moved to Pecos to be closer to my sister and her family. Pecos was a famous Wild West town on the old Butterfield Stage line to Santa Fe. Its expanse of desert and sagebrush was now populated by oil pumps and refineries rather than Comanches, outlaws, and Texas Rangers. The change in climate and culture was too much, and we didn't like it. The next spring, we returned to Munday.

We moved into a little white two-bedroom house not too far from Main Street and the post office. It was a nice house with indoor plumbing, a garden space, and a yard. Our social status climbed following the move, and I suddenly became more popular. On my eighth grade graduation, not one but two of my classmates asked me for a date.

I began taking home economics in school and made some pajamas. They were pink and black! Then I wanted to make a squaw dress. They were very popular then. Mom let me pick out the fabric, and I choose a vivid red and gold rick-rack for the trim. It was quite expensive because the dress required a lot of fabric. The skirt was tiered, and each tier was gathered separately and then sewn together and finally attached to a waist band. It was quite an undertaking even for an experienced seamstress, much less a novice. But with Mom's help and the vision of wearing it on a Saturday night date, I finished it.

Wearing the dress made me feel like a princess. In fact, every time I wore that dress, I felt very special and feminine. I kept it for years and received many compliments. The experience taught me that investing time in something lasting not only helps develop and fulfill a person but also gives pleasure to others as well as yourself in years to come. Besides, it's a great way to offset feelings of depression or loneliness. That was my brother M.J.'s remedy when someone was depressed. He'd say, "Do something—just anything but do something." I guess the activity focuses you and gets your mind off your troubles. It certainly did in my case.

I also studied cooking at school. One day I wanted to cook for my brother and Mom to show them what I had learned. I decided to fix "eggs à la goldenrod." It took me a long time. First, I boiled the eggs and let them cool. Then I prepared a white cream sauce (flour, milk, salt, oil) and added the egg whites which had been chopped fine. Then I poured that over toast which had been cut on the diagonal. Then I crumbled the egg yolk and sprinkled it over the top of the toast. The yellow color of the egg yolk contrasted nicely with the white of the cream sauce. When I finally got it ready, Hoke and Mom laughed their heads off. They couldn't believe I went to so much trouble for eggs and toast!

I was deeply hurt. My interest in cooking waned for many years, and I became preoccupied with other things. The other twin, Little Hoke, had bought an old Ford sedan—and I was always pestering him to let me drive it, and he never would.

One day he and Mom went to Knox City, a town about twelve miles away, and for some reason, the car was left in the front of the house. He took the keys with him, of course, and disconnected the starter wires to make sure no one drove it. From conversations between my brothers and their friends, or perhaps from seeing them do it at some point, I knew the car could be "wired"—started up without a key. After they left, I went out, put the wires back together, and got the car started. Then I picked up some friends and drove it all over town, waving at everyone and stopping here and there to go inside a store and visit people. They'd say, "Well, Barbara Gale, I didn't know you could drive!" as everyone pretty much knew everybody else in town. And I'd say, "Oh yes," though I'd never had a driving lesson in my life. It's a wonder I didn't kill myself!

I was a little shaky when I finally parked the car back in the yard. I knew someone would tell Little Hoke I'd been driving the car. Or else he'd notice all the gas was gone. When he came in, I mustered the courage to tell him what I'd done. I was a little scared. But he didn't punish me. He said since I was honest enough to tell him about it, he'd let it go. But Mother wasn't so sure that was a good idea. At that time I thought Mother was unreasonable. I hadn't yet learned that having harmonious relationships with others and thinking of their needs and happiness are far more important than satisfying individual wants and make you much happier in the long run.

Love and Marriage

My early sexual education was very repressive. In church I'd been taught that making love (having intercourse) was bad. Then when one day when Margaret and Jacqueline told me how children were born, I couldn't believe it. I couldn't believe my parents were sinners and especially not my sister who was now a mother herself. Jacqueline said, "That's how children are born!" I said, "No, it isn't. My mother would never do that." We ended up in a fight over it. And it was sometime later before I could integrate this new information.

When I became a teenager, the twins (as most older brothers do) appointed themselves to help Mother guide my development. However, they disagreed about what I was to do. One brother thought I should be allowed to date only local guys, and the other brother thought I should be allowed to date guys from out of town. One thought I should be allowed to stay out until ten-thirty, and the other thought I should be in by ten. Both brothers agreed on one thing— that I should be allowed to date. They were very interested in girls and naturally thought I should be interested in boys. I was.

My own behavior up until then was impeccable. What can you do when you're thirteen? I went to school and excelled in my first year in algebra, enjoyed biology and learning to cook and sew, and tried out for the basketball team. We had no car so I didn't go to any activities outside the home except at church and had little opportunity to "sin." So I reigned on my pulpit of righteousness for another year or so when "the devil tempted me" beyond my capacity to resist.

It happened like this. On a double-date, I met a boy named Keith who was from Goree, a town about six miles away. While that distance doesn't sound like much in this day and age, it increased his appeal markedly then to be from so far away. He was two years older than I was and had black hair and thick brows which curved gently over his dark eyes. Slender, always well groomed, and with an easy smile that showed his beautiful teeth, he drove a '51 black Chevrolet which belonged to his Mom. The first evening we met, we exchanged the dates we had come with.

Pretty soon Keith and I were seeing each other once a week. Feeling so mistreated at home (such as having to iron big baskets full of clothes for my brothers), and weary of fussing and fighting, I began to live for the times Keith and

I spent together. After we'd been seeing each other once a week for some months, we began talking about marriage and in early summer of 1954 decided to ask our parents if we could marry.

I finally got up the courage to ask Mom about it one night before we went to sleep. (I was still sleeping with my mother!) She said she'd have to think about it. At first, she wouldn't hear of it. She said I was too young. Then she thought better of it and the next day told me she guessed it would be all right. While the days of "shotgun" weddings in the West were passed, when a couple who'd been seeing each other as long as we had asked to marry, there was always some consideration that the hopeful bride might be in a motherly way. Our mothers met and talked it over and planned a small home wedding, and within two weeks we were married.

I was only fifteen at the time, but my relative youthfulness was no barrier. Mother had married at the same age, and in the Southwest it was common for girls to wed early. Mother went out of her way to get me some new clothes and to make a cake and some punch. His mother took us to Wichita Falls to buy rings and a string of pearls. My sister Dot and her husband came from Pecos, and she served as the matron of honor. Some of Keith's relatives came from nearby. The minister from the First Baptist Church performed the ceremony, officially closing the doors of my childhood.

Up until now, my life had its share of adversities. But there were many good times to balance them out. I had always been taught that a person reaps what they sow and that faith and hard work would ultimately be rewarded. The words of the Southern spiritual, "Bringing in the Sheaves" expressed the feeling of joyful expectation I felt preparing for a home of my own.

Sowing in the morning, sowing seeds of kindness,
Sowing in the noontide and the dewy eve;

Waiting for the harvest and the time of reaping,
We shall come rejoicing bringing in the sheaves.

Bringing in the sheaves, bringing in the sheaves,
We shall come rejoicing bringing in the sheaves;
Bringing in the sheaves, bringing in the sheaves,
We shall come rejoicing bringing in the sheaves.

4.

Fallen Angel

Rope the cow, brand the calf
Swing your honey once and a half.

I N GOREE, WE SETTLED DOWN IN A LITTLE PLACE that had
been converted to a garage apartment. It was clean and
neat and had a small kitchen and bath. It rented for $35
a month. Keith was a senior at Goree High that year and
played on the basketball team where he became a star. He did
well in school and had several close friends. They sometimes
worked on cars in the evening or went fishing or hunting.
I went rabbit hunting with them once but couldn't stand it.
Killing an animal for sport seemed cruel and barbaric to me.
We chased the rabbit across the field in a pickup, and then
when they stopped and looked into the headlights, one of the
guys would shoot at them. Fortunately, the rabbits had a
wisdom of their own and escaped unharmed. I enjoyed
Keith's mother a lot. She was the assistant postmaster. She
liked me too and so did his aunts and uncles. We fell into a
comfortable domestic routine, and our marriage was off on a
fairly happy note.

I transferred to the local high school and continued my
studies. I studied hard and won the district spelling bee as
well as first prize in a sewing contest. I also became a
majorette. The year before, in Munday, I played a clarinet in
the high school band. The director encouraged me to try out
for majorette, and it appealed to me more than just marching
with the band. But it was an impossible dream at that time.
I didn't know how to twirl a baton or have any money for
a uniform. Yet in my mind, I pranced and twirled and pivoted

before the whole school, my teachers, family, and friends.
I received a baton as a gift from the Tidwell family I used to
visit on Sundays and began to practice every day out on the
lawn. That fall, after moving to Goree, I tried out for majorette and was chosen along with several local girls. My
mother-in-law generously contributed the majorette uniform
and white boots. We performed every Friday night at the
football game. The experience taught me the power of
thoughts and gave me confidence in realizing my dreams.

Although after marrying I felt more secure than I had for
a long while, my physical health began to deteriorate. I
started getting sore throats more frequently and took penicillin lozenges. I also had fever blisters in my mouth and
severe menstrual cramps. I tried heating pads, aspirin, and
Midol—the first medication I used beside penicillin. The
cramps were so bad that once I was taken to Dr. Eiland, our
family doctor, in Munday. He gave me some medicine which
knocked me out. I was awakened about 4 P.M., when my
husband and his mother came to see about me.

The first year of my marriage I also developed cysts on my
ovaries. A doctor in Wichita Falls examined me, shook his
head, and said he didn't know what he would tell his daughter
if she had a similar condition—whether he would operate or
wait to see if they went away. He didn't know what caused
them. We decided to wait and see what happened. The cysts
went away and came back. These health problems were the
start of a recurrent pattern over the years and one common
among women today.

My eating habits changed appreciably that year. After
moving to Goree, I ate more chicken and beef than in the
past. There was a small hamburger joint across the street.
Keith and I loved to go out for a hamburger or cheeseburger.
I remember he asked me not to tell his mother. Apparently,
she didn't approve of eating out so much. A burger with
French fries cost about 50 cents. That was a lot in those days,
and we felt we were being extravagant. I didn't really know

how to cook. At Mother's I had always helped out with the
salad or sandwiches but never learned much more. My
repertoire at home included sloppy joes. To make them, you
open a can of beef, warm it up, and serve it with some
tomato sauce over toast. The only other things I could fix
were eggs, tuna fish sandwiches, salmon croquettes, and easy-
to-prepare things like that.

I ate lunch at school, and we had a lot of beef and macaroni
dishes and goulash (mixed hamburger and vegetables).
After school, I worked at a drug store. At the soda fountain
I made ice cream sundaes, floats, and frosted Cokes, con-
suming a small quota of my own on a daily basis for the first
time in my life.

Gathering Clouds

Despite my aches and pains, my health problems continued to
pale in comparison to those of my family. About the time I
left home, my brother Little Hoke got sick. He had left for
California at age nineteen or twenty and married Alice
Bright, a girl from Pecos. On a visit to Munday, he'd gone
for free chest X-rays and to everyone's surprise, the results
showed that he had a growth, or lump, and further tests
confirmed the diagnosis as leukemia. Little Hoke came home
for treatment.

I first heard of his condition in Goree. I went to the bathroom, closed the door, and prayed he might live. I also
prayed that I might come to understand how to help him.
I wrote to Oral Roberts, the evangelist, in Tulsa, Oklahoma,
and told him about the situation. I asked for his prayers and
received a nice reply. But Little Hoke's condition continued to
worsen. Mother went back and forth to visit him in M.D.
Anderson Hospital in Houston where he was periodically
admitted for treatment. It was a long way to Houston from
Munday—over 500 miles—and Mother was not too strong
from her own bout with cancer and other health problems. She

had an awful time with bus schedules, traveling by herself, and arranging for an inexpensive room near the hospital so that she could be near her son. Sometimes she stayed with Uncle Frank and Aunt Edna, who lived in Baytown, about forty miles east of Houston. They were most helpful and supportive to our family during that time.

During the summer of '55, Keith and I had moved to Wichita Falls, even further north of Munday and in the opposite direction of Houston. So we didn't go down and visit Little Hoke until about a week or ten days before he died. His body was puffy and his abdomen greatly distended when I saw him. His wife, Alice, made him a Western shirt for his birthday, but he couldn't button it. He also had little red pimples all over his body which I'll never forget. He wasn't himself and was in constant pain. As when Mother had cancer, the whole room had an awful smell in it, like decaying flesh. The doctors said that toward the end the pain would be excruciating and that even the pain medicine would be ineffective. And they were right. His legs cramped, and he moaned and suffered greatly. The family took turns staying up nights at the hospital until he died. Hoke died within six to eight months of his initial diagnosis. He was just twenty-one years old.

My brother's death caused me to doubt my religion for the first time. I knew that I had prayed as hard as I could for him and felt other family members, friends, and ministers, including Oral Roberts, had also done so. He had died nevertheless and left a pregnant wife behind. His passing shook my faith in God and universal justice. However, I had my own problems to contend with and couldn't afford to grieve very long. I returned home and resumed my studies. Mentally, I made the decision to pretend that Hoke was away, like before, and would always be there in my thoughts. I went back to my first year at Wichita Falls Senior High School and to work part-time, and soon the threads of grief were lost in the woof of everyday life.

The Clouds Break

I graduated from high school in 1956. My mother-in-law had arranged for me to enroll in a distributive education program which allows you to work part-time while attending school. In addition, I attended summer school. So I finished school in three years instead of the usual four, thought I didn't have all the courses necessary for college which bothered me. After graduation, I went to work for the telephone company as an order writer. I was a good typist and spent the whole day typing forms for people who wanted to make changes in their telephone service—either to have a phone installed or disconnected or to add or remove an extension, etc. The job proved too monotonous, and I was happy for the opportunity to fill in as teller, accepting payments of telephone bills. The change drawer was often off—sometimes only a few cents or a quarter. The other girls in the office offered to help make up the difference so the drawer would balance. But I got the feeling they didn't trust me, and I myself didn't understand why it was short when I was so careful to give the correct change. I worried about it. Then I heard of a job in the personnel department at Shepard Air Force Base. I applied for and got it. It paid $265 a month, which were top wages.

Meanwhile, my own marriage had gone downhill. Keith and I were both working out of the house all day, and we spent less and less time together. Aside from the initial physical attraction, I found we had little in common. He did not share my religious convictions and was always cussing and occasionally drank and had a real temper. And I was good at provoking it. Also he liked to go to his mother's every weekend, and I really wanted to be home, especially after being away so much during the week.

As our relationship strained so did that between us and the rest of his family. I used to feel close to his mother and enjoyed her letters and visits. But now she would send him private Special Delivery letters instead of writing to us as a couple. On visits, the two of them would go into a room together, close the door, and talk about our future. I felt rejected. At sixteen, I didn't want anyone else deciding my future, and I complained bitterly, but it was of no use. As she grew closer to Keith, I grew closer to his little brother, who was two years younger and who also felt left out of the family talks.

Already it was beginning to seem like the harder I tried to be a good Christian, the more impossible it became. The time that I wasn't keeping the trail hot to the altar in church rededicating my life to God, I was on my knees in prayer. I never knew there would be so many temptations in the world. At the Air Force base in Wichita Falls, I shared an office with three officers, dressed in crisply pressed khaki uniforms. One of them, a smooth-talking Yankee, spent an inordinate amount of time with me. I was soon infatuated with him and practically leaped over tables when the phone rang at home, hoping it would be he. The Major noticed this attraction and advised us both to cool it. I would lose my job, and he would be disciplined if we continued to talk to each other in the office. We tried meeting outside the office, but as strong as the physical attraction was, my principles were stronger. I remained faithful to my husband, and the lieutenant soon broke off the relationship. But my interest in other men certainly put a strain on our marriage, and this latest rejection put an additional strain on me.

My developing emotional problems led to an out-of-body experience. One day I was standing in the hallway near the phone, and suddenly it seemed like my mind and body were two. I could see myself but couldn't feel myself. This was scary, though it only happened once and, in a strange way, gave me some relief and detachment from my troubles.

One day a friend of a couple that we ran around with some came to town from Joplin, Missouri, which was about 500 miles away. He talked to me a lot about how beautiful Joplin was with its lake and trees and, sensing I was unhappy in my marriage, asked if I wanted to go there with him. We had driven most of the night and had just arrived in Joplin and walked into his house when another car drove up. It was Keith. He'd followed us all the way to Missouri!

He forced me into the car, and we drove all the way back to Wichita Falls. I had yet to see the beautiful lakes of Missouri. Needless to say, the return trip was unpleasant. At home our conflict intensified, and I felt trapped and resentful. As my eighteenth birthday approached, I began to wonder, "Is this all there is to life?"

For help, I spent time looking for a minister to talk to. I would walk in the neighborhood to nearby churches. Eventually Keith filed for divorce. My brother M.J. came to get me. We got a lawyer and countersued. The divorce was granted. Fortunately we had no children.

I dreaded going home after my marriage broke up, not knowing how my family would take it. No one in our family had ever been divorced, and there was quite a stigma attached to it. It went against our values. Once back in Munday, I found myself trying to explain and defend my feelings and actions. M.J. was quick to respond for the whole family, "It doesn't matter if you were right or wrong. This is *your home* and you're welcome here."

I breathed a sign of relief and went to my room and started going through some momentoes in an old chest of drawers. I guess everyone has something they do to center themselves when they're "out of sync," and mine is to straighten things. I clean out drawers, mop the kitchen, and put everything in the whole house in order. Making order in my outer world puts my inner world in place.

Though welcomed back into my family, I still had difficulty adjusting. I had work in the city and preferred to live there. Sometimes I stayed with friends and once rented a room in a private residence for a while. Then that summer I lived at the YWCA and took my first swimming lessons. At a Baptist church I attended, the youth director and I talked about my

future. He suggested that I go to college. No one else in
our family had gone to a university. Mother had encouraged
me in that direction since I was a little girl. I enjoyed studying but had no money. And I was deficient in some courses
because of my high school curriculum. I hastily enrolled in
some math courses at Midwestern University that summer,
and the minister found some church members who made some
grants-in-aid of $50 and $100 to cover my tuition and fees.
That fall, autumn 1957, I arrived in Abilene, the old cattle
capital of West Texas and now a thriving metropolitan
center, to commence studies at Hardin Simmons University.

College Days

Hardin Simmons had been founded by Baptists from Sweet-
water in 1891, and three-quarters of the students came from
within a hundred-mile radius of Abilene. Most of the university's trustees were cattlemen, and cattle imagery was everywhere. The school teams were all known as the Cowboys.
The student newspaper was called *The Brand*; the magazine,
The Corral; and the annual, *The Bronco*.

At college, I lived in a three-story girls' dormitory. The
rooms were large but plain with simple furnishings—a twin
bed, a metal desk with chair, and a small closet.

To pay for my room and board, I worked part-time for an
interior decorating firm straightening samples of cloth,
waiting on customers, and helping make draperies. The
business was located several miles from the campus. I didn't
have a car, and the bus only went part of the way so I often
tried to get a ride. On the way home, I'd sit on a bench along
with other Hardin-Simmons students. Townspeople driving by
would sometimes pick up students at the benches. But sometimes I would work late and not reach a bench in time to get
a ride. Then I'd have to walk to the dorm in the biting cold.

At school I ate with the other students in the dining hall.
It was something to write home about! There was an auto-

matic milk dispenser. You just pressed the nozzle and got
fresh milk. I'd never seen anything like it. About the only
thing I remember about the food was the sheer volume of it—
there was always more food that you could eat. It was
mainly goulash—beef, spaghetti, and other things mixed
together—or chicken and dried hamburger patties.

Off campus, everyone was fond of drive-in restaurants which
were a big hit in the '50s. Munday boasted Starvin' Marvin's
Diner, but it was small time compared to this. I loved
leaving the dorm in my date's shiny new brown and yellow
Ford and going to the drive-in for a hamburger or cheeseburger with French fries and a Coke or milkshake. You'd
place your order through the intercom, or a waitress in a
fluffy mini-dress would come up to the side of the car, sometimes in roller-skates, with her pad and pencil. But such ex-
cursions were rare. Sometimes I had only a dime to last me
the whole week. I had no money for new clothes, shoes, or
even lipstick—they were luxuries. If I had any extra money,
I'd go to the student union building and get some chocolate
milk. It was a special treat.

While grieving over my divorce, I began to date a guy
named Gene. Gene was a gentle person and had an even
temper. He would come pick me up and take me to church and
to college football games, parades, and other events important
to a coed. I enjoyed his company very much. But my happiness was short-lived. During the fall, he happened to go home
one weekend to see his parents. He wanted to bring me
home to meet them and felt he should mention that I was
divorced. Scandalized, they insisted that he stop seeing me,
and dutiful son that he was he complied. After that I felt that
I wore a scarlet "D" on my forehead or breast. Only eighteen, I realized I might have been the only person in the
entire school in this fallen state of grace.

Though I didn't date much after that, I did participate in
some school activities. I joined the debating team and enjoyed
it very much. Once we went to the University of Texas for a

tournament. My interest in debate grew out of a speech class I was taking. In class, my instructor tried to correct my country English. I felt it was wonderful to learn to speak in the new, refined way. Later I wanted to correct everyone's Okie accents at home and was always telling Mother and my brothers how to say things properly. For example, I didn't think they should say "ain't." But as in the case of my religious conversion, my crusade to reform their way of talking only separated me further from my family.

Hardin Simmons University was a Baptist school, and the values at the school were very narrow. They even frowned on dancing. Once I went to a country and western dance with some friends, and Gene got really upset. Everyone was expected to take classes in theology and religious education. I had a particularly hard time in Bible class. The instructor, a minister, said that he personally would never officiate at the wedding of anyone who had been divorced. His attitude only reinforced the feeling that my life had ended. I felt I had a choice of giving up my dream of having a happy family—a loving husband and children—or giving up the church.

My emotional turmoil occasioned another illuminating experience. One day, while walking across the campus, I felt a dazzling inner light. I experienced a tremendous brightness inside my mind and knew that I was saved, regardless of what everyone else thought. The problem of salvation had been weighing heavily on me, and now I knew the truth. The experience was a joyful revelation and helped me get through the rest of the school year.

Fortunately, my health problems also started to clear up. I was seldom sick in Abilene. Even my menstrual cramps seemed to lessen. At the time, I did not connect my physical condition with my emotional or mental state, but in retrospect it is clear that after my marriage ended, many of my physical symptoms disappeared.

As time went on, I grew more accepted by people in the dorm and made close friends with a girl named Denise from

Carlsbad, New Mexico. She was caring and uplifting, always making me laugh. She encouraged me to write to my former husband and try to get back together with him.

Late in the fall, I decided to try my penmanship on my ex-husband. In the eyes of the Bible professor, I was still married anyway. After we broke up, Keith had joined the Air Force and was now stationed in North Carolina. He sent me a color picture of him in his Air Force uniform and some sand from one of the local beaches. It was very romantic, and I decided to see him again on his next leave. We met and talked about getting back together, but he told me, "You don't have the same sparkle in your eye that you had before that told me how much you loved me. Until that comes back, we can't get back together." The next time I came back to Munday, some friends told me that Keith was in nearby Knox City. I went over there and found him with another girl in the car. I asked if I could see him while I was home, and he said that wouldn't be possible. He held up the girl's hand and exhibited a big engagement ring. That ended any hope of a reunion, and I never saw or heard from him again.

At the end of the term, I didn't have quite enough money for the second semester. I had planned to sell the old car I'd bought, but my brother had been driving it to the oil fields and it was no longer running. So Mom and I went to the bank in Munday, and she borrowed $150 for me to go back to school and finish my first year of college.

At the end of the second semester, my stipend through the church ran out. I didn't have any money to continue my studies. My sister Dorothy and her husband Bob invited me to come to Pecos.

Bob was managing a cotton gin, and that fall I worked with him and Dot. I liked working in the gin, but Bob's drinking was hard to put up with. Sober, he was very good to me and everyone else. But when he got to drinking, Lord have mercy, you couldn't stay around him. For three months in the late fall, he worked hard, sometimes all day and night, to gin the cotton that farmers from the surrounding area brought in. In spite of the tensions, I made some money and bought some clothes.

That fall I took a correspondence course in speed writing and studied as much as I could at home. Once in a while I'd go to town and do the laundry or run errands. Dot had a big Oldsmobile which she let me use for necessities and emergencies for which I was grateful. My sister and I always got along well and could talk easily about different things. She always encouraged me to get a car of my own and set long-range goals. Later my brother, Big Hoke, and his wife, Laverne, moved to Pecos, and for awhile I stayed with them.

The next year, I enrolled in the junior college in Odessa, a small city about seventy-five miles east of Pecos. Odessa is a Russian name, and the place had been founded by Russian immigrants working on the railroad to El Paso. The college had no religious affiliation, and I had a wonderful time studying journalism and other subjects in an environment that was tolerant of my personal morality. I even appeared in a community play. I tried out for a part and got the star role. We practiced every night till ten, and I loved every minute of it. For the first time that year, I bleached my hair which was naturally auburn in color. As the practice for the play became more frequent, my grades slipped, and I was amused when my government professor referred to me as a "dumb blonde."

While attending classes, I lived off campus with two other young women. They had a nice house and were happy to have another roommate. One of them was already a widow and had been left with two cars, a Jaguar and a Buick Century, and I was very impressed. In Odessa, the people were fun and uninhibited. At the house, we'd invite people over to listen to the Kingston Trio and other pop recording stars of the day. We danced a little, and I had more clothes to wear than I ever had before. No one told us what to do. It was very liberating. I stopped going to church. A lot of the pressure

I felt in Abilene was off. I even began to drink a little. Before then I had never taken any alcohol and didn't like so much as beer to be around. (Looking back, it probably would have helped balance my condition!) But I felt that if I was a sinner in the church's eyes, I might as well enjoy it. I would never have the approval of the church or my Christian friends. If divorce were heresy, I would make the most of it.

In Odessa, I met a young man who became the first real love after my marriage. His name was Alan, and he was working in the oil fields while I worked in the sales or service department of a big construction equipment company. He was two or three years older than me, blonde and stocky in appearance, and had a receding hairline. We got along marvelously, but his job ended and he went home to Houston. At the end of the semester, he wrote and said he felt there was little hope for our relationship unless I wanted to move to Houston. I flew to Houston for a short visit and ended up staying three weeks. Returning to Odessa for my clothes, I moved to Houston—industrial capital of the Southwest and city of my dreams—in the spring of 1960.

1. My daddy and his kinfolk came to Oklahoma in a covered wagon in the 1890s. This picture, taken at the family homestead in Muse shortly after the turn of the century, shows my grandmother, Martha Fields *(fourth from the left)*; my great-grandparents, *(second and fourth from the right)*; and several of my daddy's brothers and sisters.

2.   My mother and father *(left)* were married shortly before World War I. Aunt Essie, her twin sister, and a friend appear in this only surviving photograph of my parents together.

3.   After Daddy died, we moved to Munday, Texas in the early 1940s. To the left of Mom is my brother, M. J.; to her right, my sister, Dot; the twins, Big and Little Hoke, are in the foreground; and I am on the right. Willard, the oldest, *(not shown)* was in the Army.

4 & 5. *Right*, running around in costume for a school play in which I appeared as a baby. *Below*, we moved to Pecos when I was in the eighth grade. The man in the Stetson next to me is Great Uncle Henry Moore.

6. My class picture at Munday's Sunset Junior High, at age 13.

7. After marrying at 15, I moved to Goree, where I attended high school and performed as a majorette.

8. The following year Keith and I moved to Wichita Falls. Here we are in front of our new home.
Page 6

9. After my divorce, I went back to school. Here I am with a boyfriend in 1959.

10. In college, I bleached my hair for a school play. I have since associated wanting to be blond and wearing my hair flipped up with eating too much chicken.

11. Mom *(center)* with my sister, Dot *(right)*, and me in our Easter finest.

12. My brothers, Willard, M. J. and Leborn (Big Hoke), 1969.

13. In Houston, I taught by day and led a glamorous singles life by night. Here I am on the playground of Travis Elementary School.

14 & 15. *Right*, I moved to Dallas in 1970 and worked as a vocational counselor. *Below*, this picture of me several years later—overweight, wearing boots, and having short hair— shows how extremely yang (masculine) I had become as a result of eating too much meat, eggs, and other animal food.

16, 17, & 18. After remarrying, I gave birth to a son in 1973, and he became the joy of my life. *Top*, with Jon at about 4 months old. *Bottom left*, Jon about 9 months old. *Bottom right*. Jon about two years old astride a pony.

19, 20, & 21.   *Top*, Jon at Easter with his father's new family.
Bottom left, Jon in first grade living with me in Santa Fe, 1979.
Bottom right, Jon living with his father and visiting me, 1985.

22. In 1979 I was introduced to macrobiotics by Michio and Aveline Kushi.

23. In 1982, I nearly died after having an operation to reverse a tubal ligation. *Top left*, for the next several years, I was very weak from the surgery and drugs.

24, 25, & 26. Friends who helped during my recovery included Lino Stanchich *(top right)*, Bob Mattson *(bottom left, shown with Jon)*, and Larry Brown *(bottom right)*.

27. In California, I studied macrobiotics with the Aiharas at their summer camp. Herman is at the left corner of the table, and Cornellia is the third from the end on the right.

28 & 29. I especially enjoyed studying with Jacques de Langre (*left*) and Ken Burns (*right*).

30. In Dallas, I supported myself for several years teaching macro-biotic cooking and giving shiatsu massage. Here I am in my kitchen preparing for a class.

31. I returned to New England to complete my studies at the Kushi Institute. Here I am during a break at the Summer Conference, 1986.

32. Later that fall, Alex Jack, a macrobiotic teacher and author, and I were married.

5.

Moonlight and Roses

Flies in the buttermilk, skip to my Lou.
Flies in the buttermilk, skip to my Lou.
Flies in the buttermilk, skip to my Lou.
Skip to my Lou, my darling.

I HAD A MARVELOUS TIME when I first arrived in Houston. I was in love. I had left the rigid church and small-town Texas mentality behind. The mystique, splendor, and glamour of Houston—the new energy and high tech capital of the country—added to the excitement. My boyfriend Alan took flying lessons and asked me if I wanted to fly home and visit my family. I was thrilled. He rented a Piper Cub for the occasion. I'd been up with him before and he was extremely cautious, always checking the fuel and other things carefully before taking off. We took off—just the two of us—in the little plane, flew across the vast midsection of the state, and touched down at a small landing strip in Munday. Someone came out to meet us. I felt I was a "big cheese"—the little country girl who had gone off to the big city and come home in style.

On Valentine's Day, Alan gave me an engagement ring. It had a clear emerald-cut diamond, just under a carat. My happiness knew no limit. Then one day he told me about one of his friend's wives and how she had attended Rice University. "Nothing would make me prouder of you than for you to have a degree from Rice University," he told me. His friends also played bridge, which I didn't. Over the summer, he completed his own undergraduate studies. It became clear

that if I wanted to please him, I would have to finish my
studies and learn how to play bridge.

While working as a secretary in downtown Houston, I
went to the library and researched scholarships and loans.
I found I was eligible for a small grant to children of World
War I veterans. I applied and got it. It covered tuition and
fees. A second scholarship helped with room and board. Then
I also sold magazines around the apartment complex where
I was living to raise money for other expenses.

In the fall, I enrolled at Texas Tech University in Lubbock.
Lubbock was located far to the north in the Panhandle. It was
closer to my Mother's home in Munday, only 140 miles. In
the West that distance was "just down the road apiece," and
people thought nothing of driving three to four hours to visit
friends or relatives or to go shopping at the nearest fair-size
town. Lubbock's best known resident was not a scholar or
rancher but a musician, rock 'n roll star Buddy Holly. Holly
and J.P. Richardson of Houston, the legendary "Big Bopper,"
died in a tragic plane crash in February, 1959, and the whole
city was plunged into grief.

Compared to Rice University, which was too expensive,
the University of Texas, which was too big, Odessa Junior
College, which was too small, and Hardin Simmons University, which was too religious, Tech was the perfect place
for a young woman to get her college degree. I decided to
become a school teacher and enrolled in the basic teachers'
education program. I heard that during the Depression,
teachers kept their jobs and had food when no one else did.
Also, I always enjoyed children and liked the idea of having
holidays and summers off. Meanwhile, Alan left for the East
Coast. He had been admitted to George Washington University Law School in Washington, D.C. and planned to
become a patent attorney.

In Lubbock, life stabilized for me. The country in the
Panhandle was very beautiful, with vast fields of wheat and
other grains, and the campus itself had nice old buildings and

well maintained lawns and a huge modern student union building where I had my first bridge lesson between classes. Nearby Deaf Smith County later became famous as the home of Arrowhead Mills, one of the major organic, natural foods companies in the United States. Compared to the rest of Texas, the northern plains were very temperate. Elsewhere it stayed between 85 or 90 degrees in the evening most of the summer, but in Lubbock it began to cool off at night in late August. In the winter, it even snowed, and I enjoyed trudging through the snow in tall boots and exchanging snow balls with friends.

On campus, I lived in a girls' dorm. Not having boys around was a new form of culture shock. After being out on my own for the last few years, I also resented the 10 P.M. curfew, but after a few unsuccessful attempts at getting approval to live off campus, I adapted and had a good time. I attended some football games and parties. Once I made a Hawaiian luau costume for a fraternity party. It was great fun. The Twist was popular then. I went to a few fraternity dances and "twisted the night away"—or at least till 10 P.M.

To pay for my room and board, I got a job in Lubbock with a man who made tombstones and grave markers. He also did marble dresser tops and bathroom vanities. The day I went out for the job, it was pouring rain. He was in the back sand-blasting something, and when he finished, he came over to me and asked a few questions. Then he smiled at me. "Well, young lady," he drawled, "if you need to work bad enough to come out in this weather, you can have the job."

My new employer's name was Mr. Browder, and he and his wife befriended me over the next two years. They invited me to dinner often. We always ate in the dining room, and the table would be set with fine crystal and china and beautiful sterling. It was lovely as was the rest of their house. The Browders also welcomed me into their home during semesters when the dorm was closed even if they were away. They always left the refrigerator fully stocked and a key to their car. I always slept in the "blue room"—a room that got its name from the soft blue bedspread and blue draperies that screened out the morning sun. I deeply appreciated their trust and friendship. Mr. Bowder, knowing I had no car, used to pick me up on his way back to work from his lunch at home and drop me off on his way home in the evening. At the office, I typed and answered the phone. I also combed the newspaper for death notices. When someone died, I would send their family a letter or brochure about our services.

I liked working with people and midway through my studies went to a vocational counselor and took some aptitude tests. Prior tests had shown an aptitude for the secretarial and accounting fields and mechanical activities. We talked about my taking some courses in business. He told me I could study either business or education but not both. I knew I had enough money and a job for a year to get my educational degree, so I stuck with that. At graduation, my sister Dorothy and her husband, Bob, came up from Pecos and brought Mother with them. We all met at the Browders. It was a big event, as I was the first person in the family ever to finish college.

As a result of my scholarships, a student loan, and part-time work, as well as a frugal way of living, I left school with more money than when I entered. I returned to Houston in the fall. On campus I interviewed and already had a teaching job lined up. I also had a place to live with the two young women I'd shared an apartment with my first time in Houston.

In Houston, Alan and I got together at Christmas. We attended holiday parties and spent a memorable New Year's Eve together, recommitting ourselves to the relationship and marveling at how well we got along even after being away from each other so much. At one point he mentioned that he could use his new circumstances for "social climbing" by selecting a mate from a prominent family but that, of course, he wouldn't because he loved me too much. At the airport,

I cried when he left to return to D.C. Perhaps I had some premonition that I would never see him again.

We continued to correspond throughout the spring. He wanted me to come to Washington and work until he finished his law degree. I asked him about teaching in the local schools. He said that there was a lot of turmoil in the D.C., Maryland, and Virginia school systems then because of court orders to desegregate. The thought of moving so far from home and teaching in an atmosphere of protest and violence without a definite marriage commitment was more than I could bear. I pushed for a commitment. Finally Alan wrote me a letter saying there comes a time when one must "either fish or cut bait," and under the circumstances, he'd decided to cut bait.

Breaking up again was a devastating experience for me. I didn't understand a man's nature at that time nor realize that I'd contributed to the break up. In the bottom of my heart, I still had some hopes that we might one day get back together. Every so often I'd call his mother and see how he was doing, or she'd call me to see if I'd heard from him. On one such occasion, she told me that he had become engaged to a young woman he'd met out there. Her father was a prominent officer in the Air Force and had many contacts in government and business.

Starting Over Again

Part of my hesitancy to move to the East Coast and a new environment resulted from lack of vitality. In Houston my health started to decline. I simply had no oomph to go to Washington or any savings to fall back on in case of difficulties. Just getting a job and apartment in South Texas had been hard enough. In Lubbock, I don't remember a day of sickness. The worst I suffered was an occasional sore throat for which I'd go to the infirmary and have it swabbed with Mercurochrome. However, in Houston I started developing nasal congestion and allergies. During my two years at Texas Tech, I drank a lot of milk. I thought that milk was an excellent source of protein and very good for you. I felt lucky to have it and, as in Odessa, really liked to use the milk dispenser. Also in between combing obituaries, Mr. Browder took me every afternoon to a nearby doughnut shop where my favorite treat was a doughnut with a dip of ice cream on top. Eating out, I especially enjoyed a local smorgasbord which served barbequed meat, several different salads and vegetables, and bean dishes as well as scrumptuous desserts such as cherry cobbler. The restaurant offered large servings at a reasonable price. I always had a good appetite.

My condition may have been aggravated by smoking. I didn't care for the actual tobacco so much as the aura that went with it. I liked tapping the cigarettes on the counter or table and the sophisticated lady image smoking evoked in my mind. I had started smoking in college along with the crowd, innocently beginning a habit that was to prove immensely expensive, not only monetarily but also in impaired health, burnt clothes, and lost friends.

I remember wearing a beautiful yellow double-breasted jacket with matching pleated skirt. I'd just spent hours with the dressmaker trying to get the pleats to hang just right. It had cost a small fortune, and I felt really special in it. On the way to the movies, I was smoking and the air conditioner was on in the car. Some lit ash from the cigarette burned a hole in the jacket. I was sick about it for weeks. Over the years I was always trying to quit smoking and signed up for endless programs but was unable to do so until I changed my way of eating.

The rich fare I was enjoying and smoking eventually began to take their toll. In Houston, I had a tonsillectomy because of my nasal congestion and chronic sore throat. Ironically, the doctor didn't push it. I did! I would draw him pictures and show him where the congestion was, but nothing he prescribed worked. I couldn't figure out why he couldn't just give me something to stop it. He was a doctor, wasn't he? Then I asked him if he thought it would help to take my tonsils out. (I remembered that my brother had had this done when he was much younger and thought that if tonsils were "bad" they should be removed.) The doctor was reluctant but told me he could do it and see whether it helped.

Overall, my teaching went well. The first two years I taught fifth grade at a public school and was voted favorite teacher both years. The next year I taught second grade at St. John's, a private school in River Oaks, one of the wealthiest sections of Houston. I enjoyed teaching, but by the third year I was getting impatient. The students started to get on my nerves. The schools weren't air conditioned. I began working on my master's degree. After breaking up with Alan, I went to see a local pastor for counseling. He noted that I had gotten my B.S. degree for someone else and encouraged me to do something now for myself. He said it would help build my confidence. I worked on it evenings and during the summer.

My goal as a teacher was to get ahead. I decided to become a psychological counselor. They didn't have to be in the classroom all the time like regular teachers. The thought of more freedom appealed to me. Counselors were also paid very well, and I always wanted to make more money and enjoyed helping others. As the date of my graduation approached, I heard of an opening in the department of the Houston schools where psychological testing of children is done. I had to work ten months out of the year, instead of nine, but my earnings shot up several thousand dollars. But that was as high as I could go in the schools. I didn't have confidence, money, or time to get a Ph.D. Besides, I felt I had struggled enough. Once I took an IQ test before I started giving it to my students. I didn't do well on one part and asked another psychologist how to develop that dimension in my life and improve my score. Waiting for his words of wisdom, I guess I must have been very naive and idealistic. He grinned and told me to study the answers to the exam. I was shocked. My low score was on social intelligence. I later attributed this to the different way people viewed things in the city or perhaps to different learning experiences. But at the time, it lowered my self-image.

Even though I enjoyed my career, I still wanted to marry and have a family. Once I had established my career, my goal was to meet a suitable mate. As a teacher it wasn't easy to meet men. When I first arrived in Houston, I had taken a course at the John Robert Powers Modeling School. I learned about make-up, how to dress, how to do my hair, how to walk, and the proper etiquette for getting into and out of a car. It made a big difference in my social life.

For awhile I became politically active and attended Republican committee meetings in order to meet people. But they wanted you to volunteer for different things, and I didn't really care who won the election. I soon found that I was very good at picking up men on my own. I'd see someone at the swimming pool, the library, bookstore, or various other places and strike up a conversation. I even talked with guys who were dating someone else, the boy in the apartment next door, or dropped in on singles parties. About the only place I didn't look for men was in church!

Whatever money I earned during my years in Houston, I spent on my apartment, car, entertainment, or nice clothes. One of my prized possessions was a suede leather coat with a soft fur collar. One day window-shopping, a favorite lunch hour pastime, I went into Foley's, a fashionable department store, and tried on various coats. They were outrageously expensive, and I debated whether I could really afford to get one. A middle-aged man was sitting in a chair watching his wife try on various garments. Observing my indecision, he spoke up, "That coat looks just like you." I smiled in agreement and got it. The coat was full-length, but the skirts were short then so I later wore it three-quarters length. I loved it and kept it for almost twenty years.

Another favorite was a black chiffon dress with gathered chiffon that fell from the shoulders in the back in the ancient Greek style. Once at a party at the Rice Hotel, an attorney's wife admired it and added, "I think every woman should have at least one black chiffon." Another favorite was a white silk crepe with tiny strings attached at the shoulders, and just below the waist that moved as I walked or danced. Then there was a subtly designed red wool knit which always drew a lot of compliments. I didn't sew much for myself with all my other activities, but I knew a woman who was an excellent seamstress and sewed for the public. I would get ideas from *Cosmopolitan, Harper's Bazaar, Glamour,* and other magazines and let her make them. One outfit I had re-created from a magazine picture was a pair of white hip-hugger pants with bra-like top covered by a sheer black shirt. It was a knock out. I always bought expensive fabric, especially for my dress clothes (silk and cotton brocades, velvets, wool crepes, and polyesters when they came in). Double-breasted jackets were popular then as well as pleated skirts and the tunic look, which I never cared for, since I was short.

In Houston, when you went out in the evening, you really dressed up. I had to have at least one long dressy gown; street-length dresses of various shapes, colors, and styles; long white gloves that came up almost to the elbow; long and short black leather gloves; and several evening bags. My wardrobe of shoes included at least fifteen pair—three or four pairs of dress shoes, five to six pairs for work, and some casuals—and I never considered this excessive.

I also had a wig wardrobe and kept two to three of the latest styles on little manikin heads in my closet. Wigs were very popular then. I often wore them to work, especially if I was out late the evening before. My hair was very fine. In Houston's humid weather, it wouldn't hold a curl. I'd often switch from a short "tailored" daytime wig to a more romantic one in the evening. Though naturally brown, I had my hair frosted or bleached most of the time. My wigs were usually blonde, and I'd put toner on my hair to match the wig. I also pinned "falls" on my hair. These were long artificial curls that came down the front and sides, lengthening my own hair which I usually kept short.

One of my roommates disapproved of my bleached blonde look. "You'll never meet the kind of man you're interested in if you continue to bleach your hair and wear clothes like you do," she said. I ignored her advice and continued to bleach my hair. I thought my own hair terribly dowdy.

I also had one or two coats for evening wear, casual and dressy raincoats and umbrellas. Swimsuits and beach coverups were necessities as was appropriate at-home wear. About the only thing I didn't have a lot of were slacks, which I seldom wore. I always looked glamorous. With only myself to look after, I could afford to dress well. I had lots of credit cards and opened charge accounts at expensive stores and boutiques.

On the Town

To show off my nice clothes, I went out as much as possible. Since I felt I could eat anything, I did. I ate at many expensive restaurants and was exposed to many rich delicious foods I hadn't experienced before. On dates, the expected fare was thick barbequed steak. Grilled over charcoal brisquettes and topped with barbeque sauce, it came with baked potatoes and sour cream and chives, usually a small salad, and to drink several mixed drinks or wine. Once at the Houston Club, a very exclusive restaurant atop the Rice Hotel, my date offered the maitre d' a hundred dollar tip to find us a seat. He turned it down! My date was embarrassed, but soon we were sipping champagne served in chilled buckets, just like in the movies.

Another time, for a party at another downtown hotel, a friend loaned me a mink coat to go over my dress. It's amazing what a little mink does for a person at a party.

At Brennan's, a very fancy downtown restaurant, I was

exposed to more seafood. One of the specialties of the house was fish baked in a paper bag and served with a sauce which might include baby shrimp, mushrooms, and celery. When ordering steak out, I sometimes enjoyed Steak Dianne, seasoned with whole black pepper on top. At the San Jacinto Inn, which specialized in seafood, large platters of fried shrimp or oysters were served family style along with fried chicken, bay scallops, and other fish and crab. It was there that I learned how to crack open crab legs and developed a taste for this succulent dish.

I also frequented the Shamrock Hilton, the grand dame of Houston hotels. Built at a cost of $21 million, its opening on St. Patrick's Day 1949 had entered Texan and national folklore. Half the city turned out to see one hundred seventy-movie stars imported from Hollywood for the occasion. NBC radio broadcast the proceedings live over the Dorothy Lamour Show, and the crowd—estimated at fifty thousand people—paid $42 each for a Texas-size dinner of pineapple surprise, supreme of pompano Normandie, stuffed artichoke hearts, blue ribbon steak à la Shamrock, and frozen pistachio mousse. The event turned into chaos. The mayor got stuck outside for two hours, Miss Lamour couldn't be heard above the noise, and the microphone was seized by drunken revelers before the broadcast was mercifully cut off. A columnist compared the meal to "trying to eat dinner in the Notre Dame backfield." Some Houstonians were mad to discover that supreme of pompano Normandie was "only fish." City fathers ranked the hotel's debut with the Galveston flood and the Texas City disaster. The Shamrock had mellowed somewhat by my time, but not much. I remember Hawaiian luaus and parties by the pool, with chorus-line dancers and huge ice sculptures, and for dinner succulant whole roasted pig and all the trimmings.

Little notice was taken of whether the food on the table was in season or out of season, too salty or not salty enough, fresh, canned, or frozen, or preferable to another food in some way. Inattention to these matters might not have been so good for my health, but it was a benefit to my social activities and travels. Where others might have been very unhappy because they were unable to have certain foods, I ate heartily and developed wide tastes.

Eating out by myself, I would often order Chef's Salad, a large salad which came with little chunks of ham, hard-boiled eggs, and a rich oil or cheese dressing. It was so huge, there was enough food for three people. I also enjoyed Mexican food, as did most Texans, and regularly stuffed myself at Bertha's, a small family style Tex-Mex place, on the combination plate of tacos, enchiladas, tamales, chalupas, and of course guacamole salad. Less frequently, I went to Maxim's for a luncheon special of snapper throats. In the evenings, my roommates and I would sometimes go to an inexpensive chicken inn for dinner and have baskets of fried chicken brought out, served with bread, butter, and honey.

At home, when living with Orlein and Dorothy, we took turns cooking our evening meal. Orlein, a French-Canadian woman who was several years older than Dorothy and me, was the best cook. And it was satisfying to eat together and linger around the table. Later, when I had my own apartment, I stocked up on cookware and dishes, bought the *I Never Cooked Before Cookbook*, and began for the first time seriously to prepare meals for myself or company. My repertoire of scrambled eggs and fried eggs and bacon sandwiches, tuna fish, and hot dogs expanded to include a few other items. One of the dishes I experimented with was pepper steak. This was cubed steaks fixed with green peppers, tomatoes, and mushrooms in a mild sauce served over white Minute Rice. Sometimes I'd prepare beef stroganoff with sour cream and serve it over noodles. I never charcoal-broiled steaks myself though sometimes I'd bake salmon steaks.

Since I was eating out more and had more money to spend on groceries, I had desserts almost every day—and not just simple banana pudding but Bananas Flambé. To make these

you slice the bananas lengthwise, cook them in brown sugar
and butter, pour whiskey on top, set the whole thing ablaze,
and then stand back! Other times for a quick dessert, I'd
fix ice cream with liqueur. I also started drinking Coke and
other soft drinks regularly for the first time in my life. (When
I was in the fourth grade, our lunchroom was closed temporarily for remodeling and all of us brought our lunches to
school. Then those who could afford it were allowed to buy
Cokes for lunch. One week, as teacher's helper, I got to buy
her Coke all week. On Friday, she said, "I notice that you
haven't had a Coke all week and I'd like to buy one for you."
Sweet music to my ears. It was the most delicious Coke I
ever drank.)

Exotic foreign and ethnic food also competed for my alle-
giance. I dated a Jewish fellow for awhile. He was a doctor,
had nice clothes and apartment, and was very cultured. He
ordered art prints from the Louvre in Paris. He ordered some
for me, and I had them framed. I still have one of a bridge
over the Seine in my dining room. For all his charm, I found
his way of eating very strange. He enjoyed lox—pickled fish
in a jar—bagels, and cream cheese. He was always eating.
I invited him over once for dinner and began preparing a
pepper steak and some rice in separate pans. He came into
the kitchen, poured the rice in a skillet with the steak, stirred
them together, and added his own sauce over it. He made a
real mess of the meal, in my opinion, and it was a con-
tributing factor to our breaking up.

I also met a woman, a teacher, who was married to a man
from Greece. I ate with them once in a while, and they
introduced me to spinach pie, stuffed grape leaves, and
baklava. For dinner we would go to the Athens Bar & Grill,
famous for its Greek music and dance. Greek sailors from the
many ocean-going ships and oil transports that docked in the
Port of Houston would come in and perform traditional
Greek dances. As in the movie *Zorba the Greek*, which came
out about that time, they would stamp their feet in unison,

raise their hands together, and then cross over their legs for the start of the next movement. The sailors danced by themselves, with each other, and sometimes with persons in the audience. I was one who always went up to dance.

My social life also included some ballroom dancing; tennis at Memorial Park, a recreational oasis in River Oaks; concerts at Jones Hall and Herman's Park; and a baseball game or two at the newly opened Astrodome. The stadium was noisy, and not much of a sports fan, I didn't care for it, despite such hoopla as a four-story high scoreboard that flashed "Tilt" when the opponents scored and Astroturf, imitation grass that zipped together in fourteen-foot sections. However, I did enjoy the theatre, ballet, and musical concerts.

One season the Houston Grand Opera, the finest in the South, performed *Madame Butterfly*. Except for my brother-in-law's war stories, it was my first exposure to Japan and the culture of the Far East, and I was fascinated. The costumes were beautiful; the fans, umbrellas, and set exquisite; and the music enchanting. I didn't know anything about Japan or China at the time. Nor did I understand the plot. In fact, I felt its unhappy ending was overly melodramatic. But I came away intrigued by the balance and harmony of the individual artistic elements and by the splendor of the performance as a whole. Later, *Sayonara*, the film with Marlon Brando, renewed my budding interest in the Orient.

In the Fast Lane

Next to guys, my greatest love in Houston was cars. I got my first car at Texas Tech. It was a big '57 or '58 Plymouth, beige in color, with large tail fins. The Browders had owned it and sold it to me on credit with no money down. I loved it. I thought nothing of driving a few hundred miles across the state alone. Once driving back from Munday, it threw a rod. I had it fixed, but the Plymouth never worked right after that. One day coming home from school, it clunked out again and

I barely made it home. I complained about it to a fellow in my apartment complex and asked if he knew anyone with a car for sale. He said he knew someone with a Corvette. It was a '63 model, heavenly bronze in color, low to the ground, and had a tachometer plus a speedometer which registered 120 mph. The owner treated it like royalty. He kept a cover on it when it rained, parked it away from all other cars, and put down plastic mats on the floorboard. On one side of the car, he had even mounted his family's coat of arms. The little gold Corvette was beautiful, definitely one of a kind. To my delight, his asking price was very reasonable, and (as he was reluctant to let me drive it) I bought it without even a test drive.

I loved the feel of it on the road. When I'd get it out on the highway, I often drove it 75 or 85 m.p.h. I felt Corvettes were meant to be driven fast, so I did. As a consequence, I occasionally got a speeding ticket. Once I also received a ticket for revving the motor. Some policemen came up behind me. They said, "Can't you start that thing up any quieter than that?" and handed me a citation. I felt they really picked on sports car drivers and began to look at myself as a member of of an oppressed minority.

Meanwhile, some troubles developed. Built of fiberglass, the Corvette was very expensive to repair. Realizing it wasn't very economical and attracted a lot of attention—both good and bad—I sold it a year later for almost as much as I paid for it. I bought a Ford Mustang, the first and only new car I ever owned. It was light blue and solidly built, but when you lifted the hood, you could see the ground beneath it. I thought they'd left out some parts, until the dealer explained that this was just the way it was built. He said I couldn't expect it to look like a Corvette. I never drove fast in the Mustang, as I didn't feel as safe as I did in the Corvette. But it was basic transportaion and allowed me to get around town.

Houston was the fastest-growing city in the nation, and traffic jams were legion. Once a mobile home got stuck during rush hour, stranding miles of cars behind it, including a white Continental full of men in big cowboy hats. When the traffic didn't move for a few minutes, a helicopter showed up overhead and descended to the side of the road. One of the men hopped out of the Continental with his attache case, got in the whirlybird, and flew away. According to the *Houston Post*, which reported the story in a column on the life of the oil rich, the car had apparently summoned the helicopter by telephone.

I also got a taste of the jet set while living in Houston. A lawyer I was dating had a private plane. One weekend we flew to New Orleans to attend a Dixieland Jazz concert. We met another couple at the hotel. My date had led me to believe that I would be sharing a room with the other girl and he would spend the night with the other guy. But when we arrived, the other couple said they wanted to be together, leaving us to share the other room. I felt uneasy and uncomfortable. That evening, we went to an expensive French restaurant and had a fancy meal, with rich sauces and creamy desserts. Afterwards, we went to Pat O'Brien's to hear Pete Fountain and his band perform. Drinks were served —sweet but high-powered—in tall glasses. Half way through the first one, I began to feel dizzy and declined to order a second. My date insisted. In Houston I did some social drinking and enjoyed Black Russians, frozen daiquires, whiskey sours, and Tom Collins. But my limit was usually a small drink or two or a glass of wine with dinner. My stomach simply couldn't handle much alcohol, so I never got drunk. That night, as the band played on, I felt more and more nauseous. When we got back to the hotel, I became sick and threw up in the bathroom. After that, my escort didn't want to be anywhere near me. I was very relieved—in more ways than one—and we flew back the next day to Houston in silence.

Another guy I dated some years later had a sailboat. Every weekend when it was pretty, we would go to Galveston where

he kept it and spend the afternoon in the bay and then enjoy
a big seafood dinner.

I also continued learning to play bridge. When I went
after something, I could usually attain it, especially intellectual
pursuits. I soon rose to the tournament level. Games would
last four hours, but toward the end of the game I would be
mentally tired and could easily misplay my hands. My partner
would then lecture me on all my mistakes. Finally at the
"cutthroat" level, I quit because it got too tense and was no
longer any fun. In some of the places in Houston I went to
play cards, usually private homes or clubs, they gambled for
big bucks. I sat in on some of these games, but didn't bet
myself—I couldn't afford it!

What Goes Up Must Come Down

During my nine years in Houston, I continued to work and
play hard. I thought everyone did. I would stay up and party
till 1 or 2 A.M. on weekends. Though I had many romances
and exciting experiences, life wasn't fulfilling. It seems I went
from one complicated situation to another. And my high
hopes for a stable relationship never seemed to pan out.
Gradually, my extreme lifestyle caught up with me.

Three years after coming to Houston, I developed stomach
ulcers. I spent hundreds of dollars on doctors' bills, and
medical expenses began to eat up my income. I took Maalox,
but it didn't do much good. Meanwhile, the birth control pill
had just come on the market. Like most young women of the
time, I felt they emancipated women from unwanted pregnan-
cies and allowed us to enjoy the sexual revolution on an equal
basis with men. The pills were to be taken one a day for
about twenty-one to twenty-four days of the month and then
stopped to allow the menstrual period to start.

For many women, the drawbacks to birth control pills
didn't show up for many years—and then with devastating
results. In my case, the harmful effects were immediate.

Within a few days after beginning to take the pills, my body felt paralyzed. I'd be driving down the street, and the whole side of my face would suddenly grow numb. Sometimes I would lie down and not be able to get up again. I felt like I'd been drugged. I might sleep sixteen to twenty hours before the persistent ringing of the phone would wake me. I'd go to a play on a date and fall asleep before intermission. Also I would have excruciating headaches that would last for hours. Since I never had these symptoms before starting the pills, I was able to reflect on their cause. This was one of the few times I associated how I felt with what I put in my mouth.

When I developed a lump on my arm just above the wrist, I knew I had to stop taking the pills. Someone encouraged me to be fitted with a loop. This was a cervical coil that was inserted in the mouth of the womb. I nearly died when the doctor put it in in his office. It threw my body into shock. All my bowels evacuated. I spent the next 30 to 40 minutes in the bathroom with severe cramps. The doctor didn't know why I had this reaction. I stayed there several hours and finally felt well enough to leave. The cramps continued at home, and I bled for several more days. Within a week I went to a different doctor and had the coil removed.

In Houston I also had severe urinary tract problems over a period of years. I would wake up in the middle of the night in severe bladder pain. I would sit in bathtubs of hot water till the doctor's office opened and I could get some medicine to soothe the pain. The medicine turned my urine real dark but offered temporary relief. The physician prescribed tablets for me to take but no baths, compresses, or home remedies. He considered my problem merely an infection. Often, after taking the medication for the bladder problem, I would develop a severe yeast infection with vaginal itching and discharge and have additional treatment for that which included intra-vaginal suppositories. Part of the treatment of the bladder infections was the insertion of a series of steel tubes of graduated widths into the urethra to expand it and allow the urine to come out. It was very painful and never seemed to cure the problem. The urologist finally recommended surgery to enlarge the urethra and I went along with that.

I was also on medication for low thyroid metabolism. The doctor gave me extracts made from animal thyroids to make my own thyroid work better. Pretty soon I was up to 6 grams a day and could hardly walk, often passing out on the sofa. I called the doctor. He said to reduce the amount slightly to a tolerable level. I also was put on estrogen. My doctors told me that I would need estrogen and the thyroid medication for the rest of my life.

I also had chronic constipation and got in the habit of using glycerine suppositories which a girlfriend recommended. I used over-the-counter drugs too, especially aspirin and sinus medication. Once I was on sulfa drugs for a whole month.

During my years in Houston, none of my doctors ever mentioned diet as an underlying cause of my symptoms. And only once, when I had ulcers, was food involved in the treatment. I was temporarily put on a bland diet to calm me down. It included milk, meat, eggs, chocolate, cream cheese, potatoes, and other soft foods but no spicy, hot, or pungent dishes and no coffee. That didn't help much either. Finally, after figuring up how much I'd spent on doctor bills for the past six months, I decided to pay more attention to my cooking and once again sought things to read on health. Also I consulted a chiropractor. He pointed out the relationship between stress and physical health and told me to go to bed at 9 P.M. each night and get some rest. I followed his advice while eating more simply as best I could and noticed a gradual improvement in my digestion.

However, my other conditions continued to worsen. In November, 1967, I went for a job interview at the Community Mental Health Center at St. Joseph's Hospital. One of the clinical psychologists who interviewed me noticed that my hands were trembling and asked if I was a nervous person. I actually hadn't noticed them shaking before and began to reflect on the cause. Could it be the result of my increasing medication?

Finally, in late fall I found myself in a group meeting regarding some of the clients at St. Joseph's and one of the physicians commented that in his experience, patients on thyroid medication never got better. It became clear to me that the thyroid medication was only adding to my problems, not reducing them. I decided to get off medication. I read a few books on health and exercise. Without elaborating on my plans, I asked the doctor to prescribe in half gram units. Then I started jogging and reducing my medication. Running had just become popular, and I would jog in the neighborhood with a friend who lived in the apartment next door and was working on her master's at Rice University. It gave us a chance to talk out our frustrations and balance our physically inactive days, and in two or three months, I was off all drugs, including the estrogen and thyroid extract. I couldn't tell any difference in my energy level, but I felt less nervous and my hands no longer shook.

On top of physical problems, I also had psychological problems. Throughout my twenties, I had difficulty staying in a relationship and working out problems together. My love affairs never seemed to last. It never occurred to me to date just one person at a time unless I was engaged so I became increasingly confused and unhappy. Over a period of years, I visited many therapists. On one occasion, I was feeling particularly rejected and unattractive and went in for therapy. I was wearing a tight skirt, high heels, and my hair was fairly long. During the talk, the psychiatrist told me I was very attractive and said that if he wasn't married I'd be the kind of girl he would be interested in. That was all I needed to boost my confidence. I thanked him, walked out, and never returned.

For awhile I was engaged to a man from New York. His

name was Bob Anderson, and he had been working with General Electric for ten years. He was very handsome and would take me to the Chateaubriand, a beautiful restaurant with a piano bar and a charcoal grill in the middle of the room, and we would order cheese fondue seasoned with wine and served with bite-sized pieces of French bread and sometimes a salad on the side. Although Bob was relatively stable and considerate, I was often nervous and emotionally upset. We went to talk things over with a minister. He calmed me down. But that night I cried and cried. Finally, a bundle of nerves, I called Bob and told him I just couldn't go through with the wedding. We broke up soon after.

Looking at my girlfriends, I wondered why I was different. Over the years, several of them had married nice men, had babies, and settled down. I began to feel that they were more nurturing than I was. Was there something fundamentally wrong with me? I began to get a real complex. I feared I didn't know how to maintain a relationship with someone really nice. Or I was insecure and always told myself that the next one would be better.

I now realize that a lot of the problem was lack of family involvement. I hadn't met the parents or families of most of the guys I dated or taken time for many social activities before becoming physically involved, so it was very easy to break off. There's a much stronger bond between you when you have a lot of happy memories to share and know someone's family, including the home and environment they grew up in, and you can talk easily with one another about anything before you enter a sexual relationship. But I didn't know that then.

In Houston, I had essentially no family of my own, except for a cousin, Cliff Fields, who was married and had children. He was always very kind, but I didn't want to impose myself on his household. Mother came to see me once a year, and I usually went home at Christmas and sometimes in the summer. My brothers and sister all had growing families and in most cases lived across the country so it was rare for them to travel. I was pretty isolated.

Like so many people in our modern urban civilization, I had cut myself off from most of my own roots and reveled in my independence. I looked, dressed, and talked differently from the people I had grown up with. I was no longer a young country girl but a worldly wise woman nearing thirty.

Mother's Final Illness

The last time I went home to see Mother was Christmas, 1968. Though her cancer went into remission, she began to develop heart problems in her later years. In 1953 or 1954 she had a heart attack. After she moved to Pecos for the second time in the early '60s, she didn't have to work as hard, but there was little information available at that time on the relationship of saturated fats and cholesterol to heart disease so she made no changes in her diet. Dot and Bob took her to Odessa for a check-up. The doctor said the main artery of her heart was blocked and she could have another coronary. She gardened, busied herself with church affairs, kept young children, and continued to remain active.

During the time I lived in Houston, my Mother and I had gradually grown apart. I was embarrassed by my backwoods Oklahoma origins, and she reminded me of everything I had left behind. Also I was still resentful of her inconsistent punishment of me as a child and what I experienced as rejection, though she had become much kinder to me once the twins left home. Nor had she ever reconciled herself to my divorce. Once in Pecos, I took her and a friend of hers from the church out in my fancy new car to get a hamburger. In conversation, one of the women asked me if I'd ever been married. I told her I had. After we took her home, Mother told me, "You embarrassed me, Barbara. I told them you had never married." My divorce had affected her so much and was such a stigma in the Baptist church that she was willing to lie about my past rather than let her friends know.

Just before leaving Houston for the holidays, my therapist suggested that I talk to her about my alienated feelings. "Are you kidding?" I replied. "I can talk to anyone but my mother." "Give it some thought," my counselor advised.

In Pecos, one of my brothers and his family was staying with my mother for the holidays, so I made arrangements to stay with my brother Hoke and his wife Laverne. When I called Mother after her guests left and asked if I could come by and talk, she seemed surprised. She poured us some coffee and talked about Christmas and different things. Then, unable to release the past, I asked her again about my Daddy. She related the story once more of how he died, and I asked what happened to the Indian who hit him with the rock.

"They let him go," she said. "That is one thing I don't understand. Your brother got into a fight with someone, took 50 cents, and was sent to Huntsville [a Texas state prison]. The Indian murders your daddy and gets set free. There seems to be no justice in the world."

We both cried. A feeling of infinite sorrow came over me. Although she hadn't been able to talk about it, I could see that she had deep feelings about these experiences that had clouded her happiness over the years.

Walking me to the door, she said suddenly, "I want you to know I'm proud of you, Barbara," I was shocked. I had never felt she really cared for me before. She always seemed to prefer my brothers and my niece, Cheryl.

"I never meant to be partial to Cheryl," she explained. "Before he went off to the war, her father Orville told me he wanted me to take care of his child if anything happened to him. And I promised him I would."

I had always resented Cheryl, who was four and half years younger than me and so pretty. Mother rocked her and always made a fuss about her, and I never recalled her being affectionate to me. Cheryl drank a lot of Cokes and ate candy and bruised easily. Sometimes we'd get into a scrape, and I would just barely touch her (so it seemed to me) and a bruise would appear on her arm or leg and then I'd be in more trouble. But Cheryl and I had since discussed our differences and become much closer. I began to see her as a true sister and a girl who also lost her daddy in infancy. I saw my Mother in a new light as well. I was elated at her display of love and affection toward me.

A few days later, during my visit to Pecos, I saw Mother again. She said she had something to show me. From her bedroom she came back with some old pictures of relatives and ancestors. They were frayed around the edges and faded with age. She rarely talked of the past before, and I never knew the photographs even existed. She told me about the Fields family and how my grandfather had come to Oklahoma in a covered wagon and been one of the state's earliest pioneers. Someone in the house took a picture of Mother and me looking at the family album. It was the last photograph of us together.

The next spring, back in Houston, someone knocked on my door about 2 o'clock in the morning. It was my cousin Cliff, and he told me he had some bad news from Pecos. I thought something must have happened to my brother-in-law, Bob. Ever since coming back from the prisoner-of-war camp in Japan, he had had health problems. Instead, Cliff told me that Mother had died.

I couldn't believe it. I knew Mother had recently had lumbago and had suffered from that. Only a week before I had bought a new nightgown and sent it to her. But I thought she'd gotten better. Cliff related that she'd had another heart attack. Despite her own poor health, right up until the end she was cooking, ironing, hanging out the laundry, and taking care of children. She was concerned more with other people's problems than with her own. One of her grandsons who was chronically unemployed and had psychological problems had recently turned up in Pecos. Mother characteristically took him in and tried to help him out.

Mother's death was the greatest shock of my entire life.

The connection to a person's mother must be very strong because when they die your whole world seems shaken and it takes time to feel any sense of stability. I've never heard anyone describe their feelings of loss adequately, and I don't know how to describe mine, except that nothing felt right. I couldn't sleep and didn't want to eat. I just wanted to be held.

Cliff took me to his home that night, and I lay down on the bed with his daughter. She was so sweet. She'd reach over and touch me with her little hand and try to comfort me. Then the next day I felt like a zombie—calling my sister Dot and making arrangements to fly home—and the same thing once there, going through the motions, visiting Mother's body in the funeral home, and helping pick out a casket.

I was grateful for our last visit together. I felt Mother and I had come to a new understanding, and I knew that she loved me. In Houston she had written me almost every week when I was older, but I had always taken her letters for granted. Now I realized that she worried about me a lot. All she ever wanted was for me to go to school and get a good education and for me to find a good man who would appreciate me. And she liked for me to go to church. Maybe she didn't realize it, but the spiritual lessons I learned from her were greater than any church could have taught.

She had a lot of sayings that stayed with me through the years such as "Pretty is as pretty does," reflecting her value for the inner being. "You can't get blood out of a turnip," which she used to say if we wanted money and she didn't have any. Yet somehow she was able to. "She worked for 40 cents at the laundry but always had a Christmas present for everyone," Bob recalled after the funeral. "She was always jolly and never complained. She was the toughest one I ever came across." And that's pretty high praise from a survivor of the Bataan Death March.

She certainly bore her cross in life well. But what I remember most about Mom is the happy times. I remember how she used to come outside the house in Munday to greet me when I drove up. She was always so glad to see me. She couldn't wait for me to get in the house. We'd go in together. Then we'd talk and do things together, and she'd pamper me with coffee in bed and home-cooked meals until it was time for me to go.

It takes a long time to get over the death of your mother. The best way is to find someone whom you can love and share with as you did with your mother and extend love to her, taking the broad view that all persons older than us are our parents. Then you get over it more easily. It's nice if it's someone who knew her.

Mother's death caused me to reflect deeply on the course of my life. With my bleached hair, fancy clothes, and scads of boyfriends, I lived the life of a starlet. But I wasn't happy. Inside I was vacant and empty. Surely there was something more to life than making money and spending it and breezing down Houston's Southwest Freeway in a bronze Corvette convertible. And there must be some reason why people get sick and die of horrible diseases or kill each other in violent fights. Justice seemed to have eluded my parents, but maybe I could find it.

Bidding farewell to my mother, I took comfort in the thought that her spirit lived on and would be waiting for me in the spirit world with a quilt of light to wrap me in. Meanwhile, I would devote my life to seeking truth and understanding the order of the world around me.

6.

Bow to Your Partner

Turn right around, and go back through
Tie that knot like the cowboys do.

MOTHER HAD ALWAYS WANTED ME to move closer to home. After her death, I was offered a job in Dallas and in July, 1969, moved to North Texas. The move was difficult and taxed my limited vitality even further. After the movers left, I got in my car to go get something for the apartment and was so exhausted, I could hardly move. I just wanted to rest but couldn't because I had so many things to do. I thought I would never feel normal again.

Over the years, I heard a lot about Dallas. It was considered the place to be. But I didn't have any friends in Dallas, as I did in Houston, and from that standpoint didn't like it so much.

I had a job waiting for me in Dallas. I was working at a social service agency with people who had just been released from Terrell State Hospital, a place that housed the mentally ill and other rejects from society. We obtained job contracts from local industries and put them to work at a reduced wage as part of their rehabilitation process. My job was varied. I painted walls, taught classes, worked on the job contracts, and did some vocational testing. I enjoyed working with the people there but experienced stress when asked to seek job contracts from local businesses. I developed growing tension in my stomach and became aware of it both at the office and while driving to work and back in rush hour traffic.

In size, Dallas covers more area than almost any city in

the country. As a woman from New York state observed, "This is not a city. It's a sprawl." Getting around safely requires a clear mind and concentration. One day I was looking for the Northpark Mall and went miles out of the way. It was raining when I arrived, and I was a nervous wreck. Inside the mall, I sat on a bench and cried my eyes out. Some people stopped and asked if they could help. I told them I was basically all right, but just new to the area and frustrated. I felt adrift.

I looked for group activities similar to those I'd attended in Houston in hope of making friends and feeling more at home. One such group was led by a woman named Jean Houston, a well known personal growth educator and director of the Dromenon Foundation in New York. We were led in various physical activities and "mind games" to expand our consciousness. Many therapists felt that expressing your feelings is always beneficial. At one such meeting, I found myself paired off with an older man. When directed by the leader to give his impression of me, he said, "It hurts me to look at you because you're always so sad." I felt sadder than ever. There was an inner vacuum that nothing seemed to fill, especially these artificially structured encounter groups.

Remarriage

Another thing that Mother had wanted me to do before she passed away was to find a nice man and marry again. I don't know whether I resisted because I didn't want to follow her advice or because of my unhappy first marriage or reluctance to lose my freedom, but I continued to resist settling down again even though I got as far as being engaged several times. For some reason, once she was gone I thought maybe she was right. I did need to settle down. I was almost thirty years old and had nothing to show for it except a lot of adventures. For the first time in years, I opened myself up mentally to the idea of marriage though I had no one in mind.

At work I was put in charge of getting insurance coverage for our office. It was another assignment, and I never dreamed how it might change my life. In the course of my inquiries, I was put in touch with a man who handled group policies. Even though our office was smaller than those he usually handled, he agreed to come and talk to us. His name was Joe Daniel. He was very good looking, tall, and had dark hair. He dressed well, neat but conservative, and was well mannered. Originally from Tennessee, he graduated from the state university and came out west to work when he was in his late-twenties.

While arranging details of the insurance program, I took the opportunity to make friends with him. He was slightly reserved and didn't ask me out right away. But when the football season began in the fall, we started dating. Unlike many men I'd known in the past who tended to rush things, Joe took time in our relationship. We spent quiet, candle-lit evenings at a local Italian restaurant talking about our families and past experiences, our disappointments and dreams. We went to football games and dinners and parties with his friends or had them over to his apartment to watch a game. I noticed his car and apartment were always neat and orderly, and he never left dirty dishes in the sink or dirty clothes lying around. We did some shopping together over the Christmas holidays, and I met his mother when she visited him in Dallas. Once I asked him what he wanted out of life, and he said a nice home and family. I said to myself, "Boy, this is my kind of man!"

Soon after the holidays, I was fired from my job. I had been dismissed once before but had been rehired. This time was for good. For several weeks I had no employment. Then in Fort Worth, I found work. Fort Worth is Dallas's sister city about thirty miles to the west. There was an educational service center there that provided services to small surrounding schools that couldn't afford so many specialized personnel on their own. My title was Vocational Counselor for the

Handicapped. A co-worker, Bill Lawrence, was hired about the same time. Together we developed vocational training programs for handicapped youngsters and developed ways to assess their progress. We also assisted with in-service training for teachers and applied for federal grants. I loved my new work. I had a lot of freedom and responsibility. And I traveled to small towns and rubbed shoulders with people like those I had grown up with. Everyone always had time for you. Even the principals and superintendents asked you in for coffee and a visit, and when Bill and I left they would say warmly, "Now y'all come back when you git a chance."

I moved to Euless, which was located about half-way between Dallas, where Joe lived, and Fort Worth. In June, 1970, we were married. For a while we lived in an apartment in Euless, and each of us commuted to work. We spent the year looking for a house and the next summer moved to Irving. Irving is the first suburb to the west of Dallas and much closer to Joe's office than Euless. Irving is best known for Texas Stadium, home of the Dallas Cowboys. The following year I applied for a teaching job with the public schools in Irving, and in the fall of 1972 I was hired. I had been driving thirty miles each way to work and sometimes drove long distances on the job, visiting small schools in Mineral Wells, Denton, Weatherford, and other parts of the Metroplex, as the Greater Dallas-Ft. Worth area is known. Teaching young children was more rewarding, and having only a ten-minute drive to work simplified my life and left me time to relax.

Life in Irving

Our marriage started out on a harmonious note, and Joe's personality and habits contributed solidity to my life. He enjoyed a very stable routine. Every morning he liked to read the paper, have a cup of coffee, and get ready for work. Every evening, he would come home, have dinner, then relax by watching TV, especially sports. He was a big sports fan and followed just about everything. He didn't cook much but helped keep the kitchen clean and orderly. On weekends, we would go out to breakfast and run errands. In the afternoons, he liked to work in the yard.

In matters of dress, he was very neat and orderly. He always wore a suit and tie to work and dressed appropriately for social events and other activities. Though he was not one to squander money on clothes, he took care of what he bought and wore them for a long time—too long in my mind as he was still wearing narrow-legged trousers when everyone else went to wide-legged ones. But that could've been because I spent so generously of the family budget on clothing for myself. His closet was immaculate, with all the slacks and jackets arranged together and all the shoes polished. And he always kept our cars clean, waxed, and in good repair.

Joe was also very moderate in his dietary habits. He preferred simple meals and seldom overate. He was content with a TV dinner or chicken pot pie. We usually ate our evening meal on trays in front of the television. There was little conversation. I cooked more in the Betty Crocker tradition, intuitively trying to balance extremes, for example, lamb with pineapple, hot dogs with melted cheese, and baked chicken with roasted or grilled tomatoes. I enjoyed cooking very much. However, I was still lacking in vitality. When we were dating, I'd sometimes fall asleep while watching a game on television. (Once I awoke to see someone making a touchdown; he threw the ball in the air and jumped up and down when he crossed the line and I cheered for him along with the TV crowd. But I drew odd glances from Joe and his friends as it turned out I had rooted for the opposing team.) Even after I resumed teaching, I'd come home after work, fix dinner, and lie on the sofa with our pet poodle and watch TV the rest of the evening. I'd have to force myself to get up and take a shower before bed.

Joe and I were opposites in many respects. While I loved

to vacuum the house, make beds, and clean the kitchen, I
never quite got around to the finer details and always had
a cluttered desk and at least one cluttered closet. He objected
to my disorder. Then there was the basic matter of home
decorating. When we got the house, it had dark blue/green
shag carpeting. We consulted an interior decorator to help us
with our furnishings. He liked bright, vivid colors and suggested a blue/green/gold plaid sofa and a huge expanse of
green and blue flowered drapes for the den and some bright
lime green chairs. In the bedroom, he selected a loud orange
exterior. Orange had been the color of Joe's alma mater.
The floral orange drapes and matching orange bed spread
reminded him of the past glory of University of Tennessee
football and basketball teams. I couldn't stand orange, or the
turquoise in the den for that matter, and found it very difficult to relax in those rooms. It was hard for me to visualize
how things would look when finished, but I did object to the
lime green chairs, and we made a special trip to the decorator's office to select a softer color.

While our tastes were different, we both wanted a nice
home and felt that if we selected from what the decorator
offered everything would turn out well in the long run.
There were no direct charges for his services, and no doubt
he received a commission from the furnishings we purchased
at the store. I also took advantage of our financial security—
the first I had ever enjoyed—to buy expensive clothes and
shoes. I would spend several hundred dollars at a time and
was always receiving compliments on my "good taste in
clothes." But Joe was puzzled. He would say something like,
"Do you think you have enough now?" I had about three
closets full of clothes at the time. Even the slightest hint of
his disapproval hurt my feelings, and I would always say,
"Oh, I think so." But a few weeks or months later, I was
out buying some more.

Despite annoyances and minor flare-ups like this, life
settled down into a predictable routine: Joe with his job,

watching television, and working in the yard; me teaching
school, cooking, cleaning, and shopping; and both of us
socializing with friends on the weekends and special holidays.
I especially liked eating out at nice restaurants. One couple
we went out with regularly had enormous appetites. They'd
order a whole pizza as an appetizer, while one of the same
size usually made a meal for us. Once her husband ordered
a 16-ounce, charcoal-broiled steak. It was more like a roast
that he ate by himself, and he washed it down with plenty of
Scotch and bourbon. We were much more modest in our
ordering. But Joe always paid one half the tab. I protested
strongly and insisted he ask for separate checks which he was
reluctant to do. Feeling we were being taken advantage of,
I soon balked at going out with them at all.

Both Joe and I wanted to have a family. But after two
years, I still had not become pregnant. We talked about
adoption and made some inquiries. Just after an appointment
was set up, I found I was expecting. The prospects of being
a mother recharged my life. My new-found energy sent me
back to my health books, especially Adelle Davis. To make
sure I'd get adequate protein, I started a heavy protein diet,
emphasizing lean cuts of meat, tuna fish, and dairy food,
accompanied by all sorts of vitamins and supplements. I
jumped rope every day. I continued to teach and spend time
outdoors with my students and took natural childbirth courses,
doing breathing exercises and crawling through the house on
my hands and knees to strengthen myself in preparation for
the birth.

I also redecorated the bedroom next to ours and put in a
sturdy baby bed, chest of drawers in blue and white, diaper
changing table, and rocking chair with a red corduroy seat
cushion. Then I proceeded to fill all the drawers with baby
blankets, quilts, diapers, and baby books.

Even though the baby was born three weeks before the
expected due date, I was well prepared for his arrival. But
I had a lot of swelling in the hands and legs as well as high

blood pressure. One morning, while I was exercising, the
water broke for the baby to come out. Joe was supposed to
go out of town on business that day, and we weren't sure if
he'd have time to get back before the baby was ready to be
born. I didn't want to go to the hospital alone. We called
the doctor's office, and I told the nurse my water had broken.
She asked politely if I could come to the hospital. I said,
"Yes, I'll come in this afternoon." Shortly she called back
and said the doctor wanted me to come in right away. I was
afraid to go and afraid not to go.

At the hospital, I wouldn't dilate. I was too contracted and
nervous. The staff gave me oxytocin to speed up labor, a very
common practice. I had Joe throw the first pills away since
by this time I inherently distrusted modern medicine. The
staff doubled the dose and watched me take it. The medication
strengthened the contractions. The pain was excruciating.
My whole body wracked from the head down. The contractions came one right after the other, leaving me with hardly
enough time to catch my breath, much less focus on the
breathing I'd practiced. I asked for something mild to ease
the pain as I wanted to be awake for the delivery. The next
thing I knew a nurse was slapping me, "Wake up! Wake
up!" and vigorously massaging my stomach. I said, "Stop it!
You'll hurt the baby." "You've already had that baby," she
responded. "You had a little boy." The next day I was
allowed to see him.

We had already picked out a boy's name—Jon Patrick—
after my mother's father, Jonathan Duvall, and Joe's father,
Patrick Henry. Grandmother Thompson, mother's mother,
had died earlier that summer, and I went to her funeral in
East Texas. There I saw a photograph of Grandfather Duvall
for the first time. He had died many years earlier before
Grandmother remarried. He was a farmer, and I felt a strong
sense of kinship with him. Joe's father had also passed away,
and I could see the resemblance between him and Joe in the
pictures Joe's mother shared.

At the hospital I decided to toss out the sugar water and

nurse Jon myself, but he was sluggish from medication. Fortunately, one of the older nurses gave a hand and stroked and pinched him around the mouth until he began to nurse. When we came home, I was really happy for the first time in my life. His grandmother and I and his dad, when not working, took him with us everywhere. Like most couples, we delighted in his every move and discussed everything about him. But I had difficulty regaining my strength after Jon was born. My milk was not strong, and he liked to nurse frequently during the night so I had difficulty getting any rest. Jon was about nine months old before he slept through the night. Often during this time I would look out the window and wonder if I would ever be free of aches and pain and regain my energy.

While Jon's birth brought Joe and I closer together in many ways, I was still low in resourcefulness, and I missed my friends and outside interests. I found caring for a child all day long very demanding and turned to my husband for help. But when he came home after a long day at the office, he was tired too. He wanted to relax and watch TV. Before bed, he would straighten up the living room and help put away our son's things, but he spent little time talking to me or holding me.

In general, I felt shut out of Joe's life. I didn't get to know the wives or families of his friends because most of them lived in North Dallas, and they often worked outside the home during the day or were involved in their own family's activities. And at night when they got together, I found myself preferring to be at home with Jon, especially when I was still nursing him. When it was time to go to bed, I was too tired and resentful to be loving to my husband.

Therapy

After my son was born, I found it increasingly hard to talk with Joe; I felt he wasn't listening. I was insecure and needed reassurance. I studied assertiveness training. I tried to learn how to express my feelings without blaming him for them and I pushed him to say how he felt. He'd say, "I feel . . . " and then express what sounded more to me like a thought than a feeling, so I criticized him for being too analytical and lacking in feelings. It's no wonder he never wanted to talk to me.

I was always dragging him around to therapists and felt bad about it later. It went against his grain, and he only did it to make me happy. His stable nature came through as well as his excellent social skills, and the therapists often ended up seeing his point of view, though I couldn't.

Since Mother's death I had been seeking a higher truth. Therapy was part of my spiritual quest. It encouraged me to express my feelings. I needed the environment to be safe to do so. Psychology replaced religion in my life as I sought a way to deal with my growing physical, emotional, and spiritual problems.

In Fort Worth, I studied with Robert Carkhuff and his assistants. Dr. Carkhuff is an internationally known clinical and educational psychologist who was interested in humanizing education, specifically teaching educators how to respond to their students and co-workers humanely. I practiced his methods for a brief time but again became critical of Joe's responses to me, expecting him to follow the Carkhuff model. The surest way to unhappiness is to have any expectations of another person. For a time, I also studied with Carl Rodgers, another humanistic psychologist, who emphasized listening to other people and being non-judgmental. Then there was William Glasser, developer of Reality Therapy, whose method of intense personal involvement, facing reality, and rejecting irresponsible behavior, bore little resemblance to conventional psychiatry. Among them, Carkhuff was most influential, probably because of his strong personality. He taught behavioral systems at Amherst College in western Massachusetts, breaking down situations and processes into small components for people to understand. He also stressed physical vitality as the key to becoming an effective person and one's level of interpersonal skills as a primary factor in bringing about change in others.

I related to Carkhuff's method to develop myself physically and was also attracted to Dr. Kenneth Cooper's Aerobics, a fitness program that many men and women had used successfully to regain their vitality and feel better. I gave up cigarettes which I had smoked for fourteen years except when I was pregnant. Even before Jon was born, I'd reach a certain level of elevated blood pressure, get dizzy, and sometimes hyperventilate. On one of my visits to the doctor, a lump was discovered on my breast. He made light of it and told me to come back in three months, but it worried me a lot because of my mother's past experience with breast cancer.

Dizziness was my most immediate concern because it interfered with my physical activity. I went to various specialists. One was a local internist. I had a series of lab tests done that measure your cholesterol and other blood values. He could find nothing wrong physically, but since he could obviously tell that I was nervous prescribed valium. I took it for two or three days and felt worse than before. It made me very groggy. I didn't think I should take it anymore as I wanted to be as clear minded as possible, especially with a young son.

I'd read Cooper's *Aerobic Exercises for Women* and had tried to build up my endurance over a period of years. I tried rope jumping, bike riding, and jogging at different times. Finally I decided to go to the Aerobic Center in Dallas for stress testing and recommendations. I filled out reams of forms hoping to receive some effective guidance. I also took the stress test and other tests relating to the heart. When I got back the written report, I was disappointed. It had some vague summary which I took to mean I was mentally unstable and also suggested I begin on the walking program as my physical condition was poor.

For awhile I did the walking exercises, but I had no one to look after Jon. And walking took too long, 30 to 40 minutes,

so I turned instead to jogging, which took only 10 to 12
minutes. During my pregnancy, I had gained weight. I was up
to 138 pounds, the highest I'd ever been. Joe and his mother,
who often came to visit, ribbed me about my weight. Part of
my interest in fitness was trying to shed those surplus pounds.
I read a book on cellulite and tried that for awhile. It was
written by an Italian woman and advised eating raw vegetables for snacks to lose weight. I cut down on Cokes. I built
a behavior modification program for myself. If I cleaned the
house, cooked, attended to Jon and got all my chores done by
2 P.M., I rewarded myself with a Coke, raisins, and nuts.
After refraining all morning from treats and snacks, they were
indescribably delicious.

Diet and Lifestyle

In Dallas I had become a better cook to please Joe and nourish Jon and, of course, satisfy my own hearty appetite. From
Betty Crocker's Dinner for Two Cookbook I learned to made
broiled tomatoes, oven fried chicken, deviled ham sandwiches,
Reuben sandwiches, and shish-kebab. One of my specialties
was ham steak. I'd get a ham about 1/4- to 1/2-inch thick,
cook it, and serve it with a pineapple sauce. The fruit helped
to balance the meat's very salty flavor. Another favorite dish
was shake 'n bake chicken. I would season the uncooked bird
with salt and pepper, put it in a bag, add flour, and shake
everything together for a few minutes before cooking. I
always liked tuna fish and prepared it in sandwiches with cut
up apple, sweet relish, and mayonnaise.

I didn't like to cook sausage very much because it splattered
and made such a mess in the kitchen. Bacon did too, but to
a lesser extent. Occasionally I fixed the traditional pot roast
with carrots and onions and roast gravy. And then sometimes
I'd split a frankfurter about half way through the middle, add
cheese, put it in the oven to melt, and serve it with hot dog
buns or white bread and pickle relish and mustard. Once in

a while, I'd fix rock cornish hens—something I grew fond of my last days in Houston. These are small hens—less than 1 pound—roasted and basted with a sauce of butter, garlic or onion salt, and sometimes a dry white wine.

Joe liked my cooking. I remember in the beginning when he called his mother he would tell her how good everything was. On weekends, we had eggs, omelettes and soufflés, and I ate a lot of cottage cheese and pineapple. Joe never wanted me to cook lunch and insisted on eating cheese and potato chips. At night, he always had a glass of milk before bed. I drank milk and ate cheese too, and photos from this period show how puffy my face became from these items. We also had instant breadstuffs. I'd sometimes get up at 2 or 2:30 A.M. and have pop up toast filled with strawberry jam and then go back to sleep.

I prepared some vegetables but never cooked greens. I cooked red beans, potatoes (with melted cheese), and used ketchup, mustard, pepper, and salt on the table as condiments. We ate a lot of salads, including celery sticks, carrots sticks, and tomatoes. Occasionally I'd make acorn squash with butter and cinnamon or honey. When Jon was little, I also baked bread at home. It was whole wheat and I loved it. I also baked sugar cookies—a favorite—and made fudge, cookies, and cakes. One of my favorite was a luscious velvet crumb cake.

For breakfast, we sometimes had ready-to-eat foods such as instant oats, Post Toasties, Cheerios, or Shredded Wheat with milk or orange-danish rolls that came in a wrapper ready to bake. When dining out, I enjoyed *huevas rancheros*— Mexican-style eggs with chili and hot sauce. I enjoyed quiche made with cheese and eggs. Once in a while, I'd make pork chops or meat loaf. Joe drank coffee. I drank very little, just a sip or two as it upset my stomach.

We didn't have people over very much for dinner and ate out as a family infrequently. But I liked to eat out at noon. With Jon in tow, I'd have a cheeseburger and milkshake at the local ice cream store several times a week and also went to Joe's Diner, a small cafe which had home-cooked luncheon specials of meat and vegetables. Before taking the teaching job in Irving, I often ate out with another counselor at such places as the Cattleman's Steak House where we had huge portions of chicken fried steak or a local barbeque restaurant where we had thick sandwiches of barbequed beef. I thought I could eat anything the men did when I ate out. I still found myself wanting less beef, but I liked broiled lobster tails in a lemon-butter sauce. There is a picture taken after my son was born showing me with short hair, pants, and a muscular-looking physique. It was the most aggressive period in my life. I wasn't always pleasant to be around. As time went by, I found myself yelling more frequently at Joe and sometimes even Jon.

One of the ways my tightness and rigidity showed up was at the pizza parlor. We'd order something to take home with us to eat, and I'd want to eat it before we got home. That offended Joe's sense of taste. "Can't you wait till we get home?" he would say.

When eating out at a cafeteria or restaurant, I'd be through eating and ready to go, while he'd still be in the middle of dinner. "Can't you relax?" he'd say. "I don't want to rush." I would like to have waited but couldn't. I thought he was unnecessarily slow. It was many years before I could understand why I couldn't sit down and relax during a meal. That created a lot of problems.

Sickness and Health

As my health declined, my mood swings became more severe. Joe didn't know how to deal with them. When visiting his mother in Memphis, I noticed they could go for a long time without eating, but I got hungry and irritable. My emotions would go up and down. I must have been hypoglycemic. When my blood sugar levels fell in the late afternoon, I'd become shaky and irritable and experience tremendous cravings for sweets.

My bladder problems also persisted during my first years
in Dallas. During the summer, I sometimes had to urinate so
frequenty that it was difficult to travel or stay away from the
house or a bathroom any length of time. Sometimes I'd ask
Joe to stop, and he couldn't always find an appropriate place
and didn't understand why I couldn't wait. I felt that his
insensitivity to my condition was cruel. I drank Cokes at this
time, as well as iced tea, during both summer and winter, and
some beer, which didn't help my condition any as well as
plenty of watermelon, cantaloupe, and other raw fruits.

I went to a urologist in Fort Worth. He performed the
same dilations I had done before in Houston, inserting larger
and larger metal rods in the urethra. The procedure was very
painful. I finally told him I wanted to stop because they were
too uncomfortable and were affecting my relationship. He
consented to stop them but didn't want to treat me after that.
I gave up on urologists. On the positive side, I noticed I had
fewer severe bladder and yeast infections after I married than
when I was single.

In Irving, I went to another doctor's office. I liked to go
visit them, hoping they could make me feel better. But it
didn't do me much good. Temporarily I'd get better, but
I didn't like the mystique that surrounded the doctors and
nurses and their reluctance to tell me what I was taking and
what it was supposed to do. And while I loved to spend
money, I didn't like to throw it away. Once I had bad sinus
problems. X-rays were taken, and some stuff was put up my
nostrils that I thought would kill me. I would get some
immediate relief, but the symptoms kept returning. And, of
course, the treatment was very expensive so I soon stopped
it. I kept wondering what people used to do before they had
doctors and when they didn't have any money to spend.

My search for alternatives took me to Vitamin C, which I
used successfully as a home remedy. Once I had a high fever
and aches and pains and was supposed to go to Memphis the
next day for Christmas. Jon was still little and was nursing.
I started taking Vitamin C that morning in massive doses.

I crushed and melted it and took it liquified. That night at
7 P.M., my fever broke. I packed and was on the way to
Memphis the next day.

With me, everything has been extreme. From a debilitating
sickness, I'd bounce back quickly. With Joe, everything was
much more smooth and stable. He was seldom sick and if he
got a cold, as he did about once a year, he'd stay home a day
or two and go on back to work. He rarely saw a doctor or
took medicine. He has a strong constitution. Once, after
working out in the sun all day and cleaning the shower stall
with some sort of aerosol product, he got weak and had to
lie down for awhile. We couldn't determine what it was—
overexertion or exposure to some chemical. On the whole,
he was much healthier than I was.

Jon's Problems

I witnessed a lot of suffering over the years in my professional
work. In Houston, I tested the retarded, brain-damaged,
blind, deaf, dyslexic—those who couldn't read, write, or spell
without transposing letters—and the emotionally disturbed.
I taught children who had problems learning to read or write
or had some emotional difficulty that kept them from being
placed into the classes with their peers. I was searching for
others as well as myself. It never occurred to me that my own
son, Jon, might have special needs as well.

After he was born, I got a book, *Teach Your Baby*, and we
did educational activities together, beginning when he was
about twelve weeks old. As he got older, I noticed he couldn't
do the exercises recommended in the book. Naturally I felt
he was perfectly normal and the book was wrong. By then
I had learned to question the majority. I felt the book was
standardized for girls instead of boys, or there was some
other flaw in the system. Initially, I didn't pick up on Jon's
condition.

Later, when he had difficulty learning to walk and never

learned to run or climb like other children, I had to admit
that something was wrong. I renewed my search. Determined
to help him, I took him to many specialists. I took courses on
learning disabilities at local colleges and discussed his problems outside the family, all of which put a further strain on
our marriage. Joe felt I didn't accept Jon the way he was.
I felt Joe didn't accept me.

Meanwhile, my health was getting awfully bad. We had
friends visiting from Houston and I fixed them a rich peach
cobbler made with 1/4 pound of butter, a cup or more of
sugar, canned peaches, flour, and seasoning. Then later we
sat around eating oily corn chips. Not long after I got real
sick. It was like a gallbladder attack.

A few days later I went to a chiropracter. He eased the
pain some and showed me where my liver was. It was clear
that I would have to cut back on rich foods and eat more
simply. Then, too, I developed a mysterious problem with
the arm and little finger of my left hand. There was pain
extending from the shoulder down to the finger which had
become numb, and I was losing the flexibility of the arm.
Again, I went for chiropractic treatment which helped relieve
the symptom, but he could offer no explanation for the cause.
I never dreamed at the time that this problem was also
related to food.

In my searching for what to eat, I came across a magazine
article on brown rice which said that it took more calories for
the body to digest than it contained, so that by eating it you
could lose weight without feeling hungry. I managed to
locate some of this strange rice in a store. It took a lot longer
to cook than Minute Rice and was harder to chew. I cooked
it a long time and served it with lima beans and a slice of
tomato. I went to a Weight Watchers meeting where it was
recommended that we have beef only three times a week. At
first I felt hungry after meals—the vegetables weren't all that
satisfying—and I didn't know what else to eat if I didn't have
meat. I started eating more fish and seafood such as broiled

scallops in butter, but that was nothing like chicken fried steak with gravy. Still, the rice, fish, and fresh salad were the beginning of my dietary change. I was about thirty-five years old.

As my diet gradually began to change, I was attracted to the Today Church. After Jon was born, I decided there must be a God after all, and I longed for spiritual values that I could pass on to him. The Today Church was an offshoot of the Unity religious movement. Compared to Protestant churches I had attended, it was more holistic. In addition to talking about God as infinity and God within us, I was introduced to the idea of the mystical union between the creator and the creation. The church was located in Dallas on a big boulevard named Lovers Lane. At Sunday morning services, we sang a song in which "the Father and I are one." Another favorite verse went:

If I have but one loaf of bread
And I come to the end of my store,
I will sell that one loaf of bread
And I'll hunger no more.

I'll buy white hyacinths,
I'll buy white hyacinths,
I'll buy white hyacinths to set my spirit free.
Don't need a loaf of bread,
I'll feed my soul instead,
I'll buy the whitest hyacinths that grow for me.

On Easter, Bud Moshier, the minister, talked about eternity. He said that it was without beginning and without end and that we don't have to do anything or believe anything in order to have eternal life. We just have it.

Describing how matter changes into spirit, he used the image of an ice cube turning into water. He told how after death life changes form but does not cease to exist. He told how ancient masters mourned at a birth because it was a spiritual death and celebrated death because it is a spiritual birth. "The idea is reassuring since I've almost always feared death and even into adulthood believed in a hell (but not now)," I wrote in my diary after the service. "Now I think we are not punished for our earthly misdeeds in the hereafter but that the retribution is here on earth and begins with the deed itself. The payoff for cheating someone out of money, for example, might be a financial loss to yourself or it might be a loss of life fullness . . . a diminishing of awareness of feeling, a cutting off of ourselves from our Source . . . and if your life is filled with enough misdeeds, it might be like an electric light that's burned out. You still have the form. You exist but not with 'light' or life fullness."

The Today Church also encouraged visualization and positive thinking. One day after work, I came home. The house needed to be cleaned and Jon needed to be attended to. But I was feeling tired and sluggish and felt I couldn't take another step. I lay down outside for a few moments just visualizing a neat house with things in place and my son taken care of. Shortly afterwards, I found myself in the house with a new spirit of energy. I made the bed, straightened up, swept the bathroom, vacuumed the bedroom, hall, and living room, bathed Jon and washed his hair, washed my hair, and did all my usual chores. Two or three hours later, I was more rested than when I started. I resolved to experiment more with visualization methods. They seemed very powerful.

Most unusual of all, the minister, staff, and congregation of the Today Church were vegetarian. One time they showed a film on meat, graphically showing how cattle are butchered. I really moved away from meat after that. Meanwhile, I read Bill Dufty's book *Sugar Blues*, a book on vegetarianism by nutritionist Paavo Airola, and another one on detoxification using juices and fruits. Many of the church members were eating principally raw foods. I was influenced by their diet, got a juicer, and started making vegetable juices, eating more salads and fruits.

Making the change in my way of eating was not easy. As I recorded in my journal,

> I wonder if I'll ever be able to stay on a raw food diet or even an all vegetable, seed, and nut diet. It's so hard to break old habits. Yet I do pretty well when I'm alone, but when I get with [others], I don't have the resistance not to eat what they eat— and restaurants are the worst places to try to find anything decent to eat.

> Yet I feel as if my health depends on it, as well as Jon's eating habits and healthful future to a large extent. And if I could solve this problem, I could learn a lot about solving problems in general.

Some immediate benefits resulted from my dietary changes. I had been having severe menstrual cramps and sometimes had to stay in bed for two days after my period started. One health food book recommended apple cider vinegar as a panacea. I tried it, mixing two tablespoons in a cup of water every day. I got over my menstrual cramps, and the weight started coming off, too.

I started eating a little millet as recommended in *Sugar Blues*. The little yellow grain looked strange to me, and the way I prepared it, it had no taste, but I ate some of it anyway. By Christmas, I was really trim, but I couldn't stop losing weight. Still, the detoxification was clearly beneficial. I stuck with primarily raw foods and juices. Sometimes I'd prepare avocado sandwiches with sprouts and date-almond rolls. I didn't know what else to eat. At a meeting of the Association of Children with Learning Disabilities, one of the speakers talked about the danger of chemicals in food and told how the Feingold Diet had proved helpful to hyperactive children. Mr. McNeely, the current Director of Special Education in the Irving schools, commented to me later, "If you can't eat this and you can't eat that, Gale, what can you eat?" That was a question I reflected on for some time.

Joe attended the Today Church with me. He enjoyed Bud's teachings and the music, and we both liked the program for children. We felt good about going to church. In financial matters, the Today Church was really unique. They didn't hit you up for money or donations but instead developed educational seminars that appealed to the congregation. The Baptists, in contrast, were always asking for money for their building funds and foreign missionaries, though few churches had any programs to house or feed the poor in their own neighborhoods. However, Joe was not attracted to the Today Church's vegetarianism and found most of the congregation cold and aloof. He commented to me later, "Isn't it strange that we went to the Today Church for over a year and no one ever asked us to dinner or to their home?" It's true that we'd never been involved in any social activities outside the church with any of its members. He had a point, though I didn't realize until years later that raw foods make you cold and withdrawn and that is why everyone had such a hard time getting together.

One of the difficulties of being on a raw foods or vegetarian diet is trying to nourish others when you have them over for dinner. I remember once Joe and his mother, ordinarily a very gracious woman, balked at what I had prepared. She felt the stir-fry veggies and whatever else I served just weren't substantial enough to maintain our health and vitality. Another time I invited two women I worked with to lunch. We each had a half of a melon filled with mixed fruit. They were very gracious and appreciative, but I sensed that they weren't really satisfied.

I wondered what people used to eat. Didn't my parents, grandparents, and their ancestors before them do without a whole lot of animal food, refined sugar and flour, and chemical farming? How could the rest of the world be so wrong? Millions of people were not only eating the modern diet but also believed it was the most superior way of eating ever developed. I couldn't answer all these questions. Yet with the encouragement of my body, I persevered.

Real Estate

When Jon was little I wanted to contribute to the family income. I enjoyed social contact but did not want to be away from him for any length of time. Selling real estate seemed an ideal alternative. I went to classes, took the realtor's test, and got my license. It was hard to do part-time, but I enjoyed it. I made friends and some money. I netted $2,500 on one sale and spent it all on the house.

One day I came across a book on how to turn a thousand dollars into a million through real estate investments. I studied it very thoroughly. "That will work," I told myself and set about to make my fortune. I withdrew my teacher retirement, about $2,000, and found a house about to be foreclosed. It was part of a small H.U.D. development project in Irving. There was a lot of competition for these properties, but I contacted the owners directly and offered them a fair price for their equity and was thereby allowed to pick up the mortgage payments on a low-interest loan. Then I set about fixing it up. I'd take Jon and his play pen along with my scrub brushes and soap and go clean the place. It was filthy. The bathroom probably had never been cleaned during the three years the house had been occupied. I had to use chemicals to clean the toilet. There were cobwebs all over and dead rats under the sink. It was awful. I scrubbed for days on end. Then with the help of Bill, who'd worked with me at the Service Center, and Joe, who was much too conservative to appreciate this latest adventure, I painted all the rooms and ceilings. When finished, it gleamed. I had the cement people come and pour a step in the back. I had a fence put around it, cared for the flowers out front, and rented it out. It was my first venture.

One writer pointed out the advantages of buying four-plexes so I eventually sold the one family Lake-By property for a nice profit and invested in one of the few four-plexes in Irving. It was in a good location, also in need of repairs, but had potential. Being active in financing, I pursuaded the owner's real estate agent to offer a wraparound mortgage under which the owner retained the original note, and I made the payments directly to him. That prevented us having to qualify for a second property through a commercial lender and enabled me to have a lower interest rate. In addition, it enabled the owner to have a nice monthly income without the headaches of managing this out-of-town property so both were well served. I put a new roof on it and repainted and cleaned up the apartments as they became vacant. I put up curtains, fixed the place up, and raised the rent. Joe helped with the lawn work and sometimes helped clean and paint the apartments, though I always suspected he'd rather be doing something else. After we divorced and I got into raw foods, I found the stress of managing this property too much—along with working a full time job and taking care of Jon who was still a toddler at that time—so I sold it.

Who knows how far I would have gone in real estate if I had kept my health? In my experience, if a person develops material wealth too quickly, he or she will fall down. He should develop spiritually and learn how to care for his health until he is about forty-nine or fifty. Then he can safely build material wealth. If you're approaching fifty and don't have much material wealth to show for it, be very grateful. If you're in your thirties and have accumulated material wealth, please release what you don't need for the future health of yourself and family.

Family Ties

My sister Dot and her husband Bob came to Irving whenever they could. We wanted to stay close after Mother died. As the oldest, she was the central figure keeping our family together. I wrote to her, as did my three brothers, and she would circulate news of our lives to one another. Dot was conscious of Jon not having a grandmother on his mother's side and served as a stand-in for his granny. She became devoted to him and had him call her Nunny like her other grandchildren. She and Bob came for his first birthday. She'd also come to a hairdresser's convention in Dallas once a year and often bring the women who worked in her shop with her. We'd always have a good time—shopping, eating, and drinking in Dallas's finer places, including the Fairmont Hotel.

In the mid-'70s, my brother M.J. came back from Iran. He had been working on an oil project there. For a long time, he and his family were based in Washington State, where he'd been stationed at Bremerton Naval Base. In the service, he had traveled all over the world, visiting Scotland, Ireland, and Hawaii and many other places.

That summer, after Joe and I had finished decorating the house, I decided it would be nice to have a family reunion. Hoke and Laverne had returned to Oklahoma and came down with their four children. Dot and Bob, along with their son Scotty, drove across from Pecos, and Willard and Bertha came all the way from Idaho where he was working as a carpenter. We borrowed the house of a neighbor to have enough room for everyone, but it still didn't work out very well. The children ran in and out of the house leaving the sliding glass doors open, and Joe and I kept getting up to shut them to keep the cool air inside and to prevent the air conditioner from becoming overworked. Our efforts to control things only made people more uncomfortable. And sure enough, the air conditioner froze up. The July Texan atmosphere was stifling, and Joe was upset. An only child, he had never been to a family gathering quite like this. Nor had he been around relatives who all talked at once when they got together. He was simply overwhelmed by my family. The final straw was when the dog got sick and kept me up half the night with a hacking cough. We were one weary bunch when everyone left.

Social Concerns

The war in Vietnam was on everyone's mind at this time. TV brought the fighting into the living room. Eating dinner in front of the evening news day in and day out made the conflict even more real. Joe was of an age unlikely to be drafted so I never really worried about the war directly affecting my family. Some women were very militant about their husbands not going to battle. This was a new experience for me since my brothers all wanted to fight in past wars and tried anything to get into the service. One of Joe's cousins in Missouri talked to me a lot about the war. I thought she was overreacting because her husband hadn't been drafted yet. One of my nephews was in the army for a short time, but he didn't like being across the country from his mother, much less going to Vietnam, and was able to get himself discharged.

Drugs were equally remote from my daily life though they affected many families and became a national tragedy. In Houston, I had smoked marijuana once with negative effects. When I first came to Dallas, I smoked something with a friend. My mind couldn't stop reeling. I was up all night and couldn't rest. It was wild. After that, I was afraid to try any again. As much as possible, I stayed away from places and social situations where drugs were available. I didn't trust people who occasionally offered them to me and was thankful that I escaped that scene. As for hippies, I was curious to find out about them. In California I later asked my brother to take me to the university to see a hippie as there were none in Dallas.

I watched the Watergate hearings while pregnant. I wondered what the world was coming to. I entered details of the scandal and President Nixon's downfall into the baby book

I was preparing as news of the day. I felt a basic difference in men and women as far as social concerns went. My horizon was more immediate, keeping the house cleaned and getting the food cooked. My philosophy was to let the rest of the world take care of itself. My strongest political opinion was that a woman should take charge of the federal budget. I often felt we wouldn't have a national debt if women controlled the country's finances. They are infinitely more practical and suited to the task of managing funds than men. Even the most extravagant woman becomes more frugal when she's put in charge of spending.

My perspective on the world gradually widened. In Irving, we had a babysitter from Thailand. Her first name was Bootsabah. She was different than Western women, always wearing dresses instead of slacks and keeping her hair long. She liked to be at home, sew, and take care of the children. She invited us to dinner one time, and we had lots of appetizing vegetables and different dishes including tidbits of marinated raw meat. Sometimes she offered me tea when I came to pick Jon up. It was refreshing to be with her.

Culturally, I enjoyed the movies *Dr. Zhivago* and *The Sound of Music*. They opened up new vistas of life in Russia and Austria. Then someone gave me a small paperback on world religions. I read about Buddha and Lao Tzu for the first time. I learned that people in the East held these great teachers in the same esteem as people in the West held Jesus. I was amazed. Until then, I assumed the whole world had the same view of Jesus as they did in Texas. My view was that Christian missionaries went abroad to help ignorant souls who hadn't heard of a higher life and bring them the good news of Christ. It never occurred to me that there were others believed to be saviors or sons of God. Yet here was unmistakable evidence that half the world had a highly developed culture, philosophy, and way of life.

Since becoming a teacher, I identified with psychology more than religion. However, I still read philosophy and was attracted to esoteric teachings. Boots told me about customs in Thailand. After her father died, the family had a séance and he came back from the spiritual world. He told them he was doing fine, and they had a nice conversation. As my eyes widened, she explained that spirit communication was common there.

Separation and Divorce

During the high temperatures of late August, the relationship between Joe and me grew too tense, and we separated. It's true that we had differing views of house decorating, parenting, male/female roles, family, work, money, play, and food. But most couples have many differences. Largely because of a lack of patience and understanding and a lack of appreciation for each other's positive points, we were unable to reconcile our differences after six years. At my insistence, Joe moved into the rent house on Lake-By and left me and Jon in the house on Cordova Bend. Reluctantly, just before Jon's third birthday, I left him with a baby sitter and returned to work.

I continued my dietary and health experiments. When Jon was about five, I took him with me to a Hippocrates Health Center in California. I hoped the visit would detoxify us and enable me to learn more about healing with natural foods. The raw foods program there included fruits and vegetables and wheat grass juice three times a day and in between meals. In addition, we were encouraged to do wheat grass juice enemas. While I didn't insist on them for Jon, I did them myself plus a colonic or two. After two weeks, we were nearly wiped out. I got so weak I could hardly get up the hill from the parking lot to the center with Jon. And a trip to the natural foods restaurant in town where everyone sometimes went for a heartier meal was a major excursion. People thought Jon must have cancer because he looked so emaciated. When thin Jon and his thin mother arrived back in Dallas, I was one unpopular woman. What I didn't realize at the time was that raw food and wheat grass juice fasts detoxify the brain as well as the liver, causing you to lose your judgment.

I also did a liver detoxification, taking large amounts of olive oil, lemon juice, and a little garlic. I did enemas and occasional colonics at home to clean out my colon. In a way I succeeded. I would pass large ropes of mucus. Actually, I may have been creating more mucus than I discharged because of dairy food, flour products, and other foods I was still eating. But I didn't know it at the time. I did know it was not pleasant to begin and end the day with an enema. For almost an entire year I depended on enemas and didn't have a natural bowel movement. Also I had chronic skin rashes and smelled like a garlic bud. Thanks to my raw foods, I was discharging a lot of past animal food. It was really hot that summer in Dallas, and I was not using air conditioning. I still ate ice cream made with honey and yogurt cones. That winter I nearly froze to death from these cold foods.

There was one interesting side effect of my experiment with raw food fasts, enemas, and colonics. I suggested to Joe that we try to reunite our family. He declined, explaining later he no longer found me attractive. No wonder, I could wear size 5 and 7 junior miss clothes and was as cold as the food I was eating!

After Joe left, Jon and I continued to go to the Today Church by ourselves. Their lovely music and upbeat spirit helped to ease the sadness of another failed marriage. I especially enjoyed the Thanksgiving celebration and the songs they sang, "Every Day Is Thanksgiving Day," and "Thank God We Live in America." Several hundred people came. They also sponsored various social activities and educational programs. In late January 1979, I heard that a couple from Boston would be visiting Dallas and give a seminar at the Today Church. Their names were Michio and Aveline Kushi, and they were presenting something called macrobiotics.

7.

Shifting Gears

Meet your honey, pat her on the head.
If she don't like biscuit, give her cornbread.

WHEN I FIRST HEARD OF MICHIO KUSHI, I was not aware who he was or that he was Japanese. Nor had I ever heard of macrobiotics. Bud Moshier, the minister at the Today Church, had told us that he was a well known speaker on food, diet, and spirituality. He said that it had been difficult to arrange for Mr. Kushi and his wife to come to Dallas as they were booked well in advance. The Kushis travel and teach all over the world.

It was very cold that weekend. People think it doesn't get cold in Texas, but at times we have some extremely cold weather. It just doesn't last very long. This particular week-end started off clear, but it snowed and iced over before the seminar ended.

I'd become much more cautious and thoughtful about driving in inclement weather, and my driving speeds were more modest as well. It had been just about a year ago, in late January, 1978, that I'd left my office in the Learning Opportunities Center of the Irving schools to meet with a consulting psychologist about a student I had evaluated. The roads had been wet and icy on the way to work but seemed to be clearing up. Yet something about me didn't want to go.

"Oh, well, get it over with," I thought. I forgot my premonition as I listened to the hum of the motor and flipped on the stereo. I loved my shiny red Chevrolet Camaro. There was no other word for it. I relaxed into the leather seat as I gradually approached a few slower moving vehicles and glided around them without any difficulties. I came under the speedway, still well within the speed limit and turned right, entering the curve that fed into the busy freeway. Everything seemed OK. The car held the road well, and I glanced into my side view mirror, turning my head slightly to check for oncoming cars. A slight acceleration and I whooshed onto the freeway. Then I had to quickly cross four lanes to be in position where I needed to exit. As I looked in the rear view mirror, all I could see was a thick cover of ice on the back window. "Christ," I thought, "I'd forgotten to check it again before I left the office." I was in the far left lane on a freeway in which all the exits for the next forty miles were on the right. In a split second, I decided to take my chances immediately and cross to the right. If someone were approaching, maybe they'd see me and slow down until I could get across. No such luck.

I heard the sound of crunching metal and felt the car being pushed sideways along the freeway, telephone poles and trees flickering by the windows. The words existed only in my head, "Oh, God, please don't let me die." Then I felt a lurch, and the picture abruptly changed. The car had stopped, and I was sitting in a bed of shattered glass—off the freeway on a patch of dirt. The numbness drained out of my body, and I heard someone speaking to me, "Are you all right?" I looked up at him and started to cry.

My knees shook as he helped me from the car. I surveyed the damage to the Camaro—the entire right side was caved in —and to his two-ton pickup truck and marvelled that I was alive. In fact, in spite of the broken windshield and flying glass, I'd received only some small scratches and a run in my hose along with an overwhelming sense of gratitude for my life.

Meeting the Kushis

This morning, just over a year later, I got up early so that I could drive leisurely to church. As I left, I told a friend,

"I'm going to go and see what they say about spirituality, but I'm not going to change my diet." I felt I already had the perfect diet. On raw foods, I had achieved a trim figure. Since giving up meat, all the excess weight I had worried about had come off and I felt better.

Ironically, the talk on spiritual development was the one lecture I missed. It was at night, and I was too tired to attend. The seminar was divided into lectures of about three hours each. I was so surprised. I'd never been in a three-hour lecture without a break. Michio stood all the time, and he had at least three such lectures the first day, yet he never seemed tired. I had difficulty sitting for that long. Fortunately, it was a casual setting, and I felt comfortable to get up and stretch, get some tea, and come back and sit down.

I thought the Kushis looked Oriental, but I couldn't tell if they were Japanese or Chinese. Aveline wore a beautiful, pale, yellow-flowered kimono one day. Except for my babysitter, I didn't know anyone from the Far East. But it didn't matter to me where they came from. I felt very fortunate to have them here. My early upbringing and the philosophy of the Today Church had prepared me to accept everyone regardless of their background or nationality. I truly felt we are all brothers and sisters of one endless universe.

I was attracted to macrobiotics after hearing Michio, not so much because of what he said as much as by the kind of person he was. (Actually I didn't understand half of it because the material was new and because his pronunciation was hard to understand.) I could see that he loved everyone and was healthy and happy, and I wanted to be like him.

Michio kidded and joked a lot. He talked about so many things that it was hard to categorize him. He taught the seven conditions of good health: 1) no tiredness or fatigue, 2) good appetite, 3) sound sleep, 4) good memory, 5) never be angry, 6) be joyous and alert, and 7) have endless appreciation. He drew a big spiral on the board and told us about our journey from God or One Infinity to our life on earth and back again through seven levels to our divine source or origin. He talked about whole grains, including brown rice, as the principal food of human beings for millions of years and explained the Standard Macrobiotic Diet. "Is this brown rice the same as the brown rice I used to buy in the store?" I thought to myself. I didn't know exactly.

Michio also talked a lot about man and woman. Through proper food, exercise, self-reflection, and other simple methods, the relations between husband and wife could be harmonized. My first impression of macrobiotics was that it was not only a diet for better health. It also was a way of bringing men and women back together again. That part really appealed to me.

Michio also introduced visual diagnosis and showed us how to evaluate our own health by examining the features of the face and body. We looked into each others' eyes, bent our hands, and pressed the area between our forefingers and thumbs, looking for green coloring in certain areas and searching for faces that looked whiter than the rest.

To my mind, Michio himself looked healthy and fit. But not everyone thought so. One church member thought he was too thin. It was true he didn't have an ounce of fat, but in my book that was a plus. What really impressed me besides his stamina was his infinite patience in answering all the endless questions that came up.

Bancha tea was served at the seminar. I tried it and thought it had no taste. We were accustomed to having herbal teas with a little honey at the church. Other than that, no macrobiotic food was served. I don't know where everyone ate, but I ate lunch at a nearby vegetarian restaurant during the meal break. Later in a bookstore, I picked up a copy of Michio's *The Book of Macrobiotics*. But most of it I couldn't read. It was too complicated and analytical for me at the time. I couldn't get into the diagrams, but I loved the part on family and spiritual values and read it often during the years to come. It was several years before I could read and understand the book as a whole.

Aveline, Michio's wife, looked very pretty. She often sat in the back of the auditorium, knitting patiently while her husband talked. I enjoyed Aveline's presentation very much. She was so small but had such grace, charm, and energy. After all the dishes were cooked, she passed them around for the class to taste. The food was attractive—really a work of art in itself—but I didn't have any. I was fasting until mid-afternoon. During his talk the day before, Michio had mentioned that most people, including many vegetarians, suffered from worms. Afterwards, I went up and asked him if I had them. He looked for a few moments at my finger nails and said I did. He was an expert at Oriental visual diagnosis and could tell at a glance everything about a person's health. From a ridge in my nail, he could see that I had intestinal worms or parasites. I chose immediately to begin a traditional remedy used in the Far East for thousands of years: to skip breakfast and lunch, and when true hunger set in, to eat a handful of raw pumpkin seeds mixed with grated raw scallions and to chew some raw rice.

During the seminar, I noticed a small group of people in the church sitting up front. They looked different from everyone else. They were dressed casually, with neat, simple, cotton fabrics, and one had a beard. I was drawn to them even though they were in their early twenties and I was nearly forty. In the course of his lectures, he called them onto the stage to illustrate different points. I soon learned these people were already macrobiotic and had been studying with the Kushis or following their teachings for some time.

After Aveline's class was over, I went to the local health food store. I bought some brown rice, umeboshi plums, seaweed, and other basics. I ran into someone who had been at the seminar, and he helped me locate the items I hadn't heard of and gave me a few more tips on preparing different things and a few precious words of encouragement. My macrobiotic odyssey had begun.

Starting Macrobiotics in Dallas

Community may not be the right word to describe the few
people in Dallas and North Texas practicing macrobiotics.
Solitary individuals and couples came together every so often
for a potluck or a seminar. But then life in Texas had been
like that for generations. Hardy pioneer families had carved
isolated homesteads and ranches across the face of the land.
For weeks and months, they might not see another human
being, and then at planting, harvest time, or the holidays
everyone would get together for a big square dance, jambo-
ree, or rodeo.

I first met Norman Ralston at Michio's seminar. A veterinarian in Balch Springs, just east of Dallas, he was the best
known macrobiotic practitioner in the area. He had pioneered
in feeding natural foods to dogs and cats and had successfully
used the Oriental philosophy of yang and yin (the contractive
and expansive qualities that make up all phenomena) to
treat the animals at his clinic. He was one of the first to use
acupuncture on animals, and whenever possible he preferred
a home remedy over a modern drug or chemical. For hair-
balls, for example, he would give a cat slippery elm bark, a
traditional herb used by the Indians.

In his late fifties, Norman was short and stocky and active.
He also had an endless store of humorous stories and anec-
dotes about growing up in Texas and learning more about
medicine from his grandmother and people who had formerly
been slaves than from doctors at veterinary college. He was
the epitome of the country doctor, and so many people came
to him for advice that he had to tell them he only treated
animals. Not surprisingly, some of the people whose cats and
dogs he helped with brown rice, miso soup, and seaweed
took a fancy to the diet after seeing their pets recover. The
same year I met him *East West Journal* put a picture of
Norman and a dog on the cover and ran a long interview

with him about a macrobiotic approach to pet care. The issue immediately sold out and became a collector's item.

Norman and his friend Helen (who later became Mrs. Ralston) had helped plan and sponsor the Kushis' seminar. Helen sat at the desk, helping enroll people and answering everyone's questions. Later I would become close friends with them both.

Another person I met at the seminar was Terrance Luster. He lived in Denton, a small college town north of Dallas, where he ran a small co-op that carried whole grains and macrobiotic books and supplies. I introduced myself, and as we chatted it came up in conversation that I was divorced and didn't have a boyfriend.

"No wonder. You look like a carrot," he said. "No one wants to date a carrot. They want to date a human being."

He was referring to my skin color. It was bright orange. On my raw foods diet, I had been drinking about a half gallon of carrot juice a day. I thought it would cleanse my liver and then the orange color would go away. But it didn't.

Crushing as his remarks were, Terrance's good humor and acceptance softened their effect and left me with some hope. He introduced me to Gwen, his fiance. She said they might be giving some cooking classes in the future. Later on, Gwen and I became friends, and my skin color gradually returned to normal.

I started to put the Kushis' principles into practice immediately. I knew some of the foods in the Standard Macrobiotic Diet, but not many. I was already familiar with brown rice, millet, and oatmeal, but I had never had whole oats, whole wheat berries, or buckwheat. I had never even seen or tasted barley before. Nor had I ever tried seaweed except for powdered kelp. I'd never cooked collard greens, mustard greens, bok choy, nappa cabbage, butternut squash or any of the hard winter squashes except for acorn squash. I had never heard of azuki beans or chickpeas. The only macaroni I'd eaten had been covered with cheese. And tuna, the one fish I'd eaten most frequently, was not among those on the approved list.

At home after the seminar, Joe helped me remove the $700 Norwalk juicer from my kitchen to a more appropriate place in the garage, and I cleared out the Haagen Daas, carrot-juice, fruits, lettuce, and other cold foods from the refrigerator and put the new food away.

Monday night I cooked a bowl of oatmeal and some pinto beans. It was the first cooked food I'd had in a long time. It was so delicious and filling. I realized in the cold of winter my body was starving for warm food. It became laughable in a way later when I looked back at all the cold foods I had been taking. No wonder I was cold all the time. But it spoke of the miracle of our bodies and life itself that we do survive in spite of some gross mistakes and that once we admit our errors and change our ways, our bodies are wonderfully forgiving. Later I also came to see that my raw foods diet had made me too yin—weak, unfocused, and prone to accidents, like my collision on the freeway.

In the beginning, my understanding of the macrobiotic diet was somewhat faulty. During his talks, people would ask Michio what caused this or that sickness to develop or symptom to appear. He would say, "Too much chicken," "too many eggs," "too much meat," "too much cheese," "too much salt." All these foods were too yang—extremely contractive, tightening, dry, and warming. Conversely, he would say other diseases were caused by "too much ice cream," "too much sugar," "too many fruits," "too many fruit juices," and "too much milk." Foods like these were too yin—overly expansive, relaxing, moist, and cooling. From this I got the general idea of the two broad categories of foods to avoid. But I thought it was all right to have all these things once in a while—just not "too much" of any extreme. Also someone asked Aveline if it was all right to drink *sake* (Japanese rice wine) or regular wine. She said it was all right occasionally if it was good quality. Naturally I went right out and bought some.

The first week I had too much tamari soy sauce. I would put it on brown rice at the table, on noodles, on vegetables, and practically everything else. It made them taste so much better. Then I had my first Coke in at least a year. I didn't realize it at the time but tamari is very yang. If you take too much, you naturally are attracted to strong yin—such as Coca-Cola. Later when I took cooking classes, I learned that tamari soy sauce (in small volume) is generally added to foods while they are still cooking and not at the table.

The following week I had severe cramping and pain in my lower abdomen. I located a physician who had impeccable credentials and some background in psychology. His office was located behind the health food store, and I halfway hoped there was some connection. Upon examination, he found my urine was clouded with "pus" and found two huge "masses" on my ovaries. He implied they would have to come out and wanted to schedule me for immediate surgery.

I was shocked. After so many years of searching, I had finally found what I was looking for—macrobiotics—but maybe it was too late. From past years of dietary abuse, I might now have cancer and it could be too late to reverse it, even with proper eating.

I didn't know what to do. I told the doctor, "Can't you go in and see if they are malignant and then let me decide if I want to have surgery?"

He said, "No, I have to have your signed permission to operate before I go in."

I asked him if I could wait till Jon's grandmother got back to town. She was due back in a few days, and I wanted my son to be with someone that I trusted and knew he felt comfortable with. Based on my previous experience, the whole thing seemed too risky to me. And there wasn't anyone I could ask to come to the hospital and be with me while I recuperated.

"No," the doctor told me again. "We have to put you in immediately."

As politely as I could, I declined the surgery.

The doctor was flabbergasted. He'd had a lot of training. He'd studied Gestalt therapy and nutrition in addition to his medical training as a gynecologist. He was belligerent when I questioned his authority. He insisted on me signing some papers before I left the office—papers saying I wouldn't hold him responsible for renal failure. The receptionist at the desk looked at me like some poor, pathetic creature when I left.

I was shaken by the fear of cancer, the mucky urine specimen I had produced, and the emotional despair of being alone. But I had had it with modern medicine. Even though I was still in pain and thought I could die, I felt there must be some other way. Then I remembered I wasn't really alone any more. I went home and called Jerry Austin, whom I also had met at the seminar. Jerry had been practicing macrobiotics for some time.

Jerry told me he thought I had switched too suddenly from extreme yin (cold, raw foods) to yang (warm, hot foods). The rapid change in diet might have something to do with my problems. In macrobiotics, they called it a discharge. A lot of the excess from the past would come out as you started to eat better. The kidneys and liver, which filtered the blood of impurities, were affected most often. This was what was probably causing the pain and pus to show up in my urine.

Jerry talked to Terrance. They recommended I still eat some of the things I was accustomed to, such as a few fresh salads, until I got more used to cooked grains and vegetables. Gradually, my pain should go away. As for the masses on my ovaries, they said not to worry too much about them. Many women had experienced complete recoveries from cysts and tumors in the ovaries or uterus after becoming macrobiotic. In any case, they were usually slow growing and shouldn't be enhanced by my new way of eating.

Greatly relieved, I continued my new diet. I started studying with Jerry and later with Terrance and Gwen in Denton.

It was a long drive, thirty-eight miles each way, but I was
so happy the distance didn't matter.

Jerry had a simple apartment with the barest furnishings
and cookware and dishes, yet he turned out the most wonderful meals. There were hearty stews, tasty sauces for the
grains, baked squash, and occasional desserts. I couldn't see
how he could cook at all with so much talking going on and
strange conversations about yin and yang. The whole affair
seemed more like a family affair than a cooking class. I
remember one afternoon Jerry decided to make some cookies,
and there was a big to do about whether he should add so
much tahini to the mixture.

For a long time, it was the only dessert I knew how to
make, and I ate a lot of them. They were not really the best
thing for my condition, but by spring, my pains and aches
had all cleared up. I got up before dawn and jogged at a
nearby track before cooking breakfast, fixing lunch, and
getting myself and Jon ready to leave the house so I could
be at work by 8 A.M.

Beginner's Mind

Shortly after becoming macrobiotic, I had a dream about
Michio. It was in color and very vivid. He seemed to be
telling me to get my life together first spiritually and then to
build a relationship. He said it was all right to marry after
age forty. My fortieth birthday was coming up in a few
months, and like most women—and men for that matter—it
was a big milestone, especially since I faced it alone.

As my macrobiotic contacts widened, I heard about the
George Ohsawa Macrobiotic Foundation. G.O.M.F. was run
by Herman and Cornellia Aihara, early students of George
Ohsawa, the founder of modern macrobiotics. They had come
over from Japan several years after Michio and Aveline, lived
with the Kushis in New York, and eventually settled in
northern California where they ran a center, a summer camp,
and various publishing activities. One of Cornellia's interests

was matchmaking, and she ran a macrobiotic dating service.
I enrolled in it, sending her $15 with a picture of myself and
a letter giving my date of birth, background, and interests.
She sent me four names. I ended up meeting three of the
guys. The other I eliminated because he was too good
looking. I felt that would be nothing but trouble.

Arthur was the first to come to Dallas. He was from New
Mexico and had been macrobiotic about eight or nine years.
I felt like a real beginner in comparison. He was about 5' 10"
and though he was approaching fifty still had dark hair and
was slender and had a pleasant smile. Though he didn't look
muscular or strong, I was amazed by his physical strength
and endurance. He could carry huge building stones for much
of the day without tiring and drive long distances with little
sleep.

But for all his physical prowess, he was equally at home in
the kitchen, and he cooked my first macrobiotic meal for me
outside the cooking class. He made a mushroom and onion
sauce to go over some whole grain. It was warming and
delicious, and he was patient and answered my questions
tirelessly.

Unfortunately Arthur didn't seem nearly as pleased with
my condition as I was with his. I still had a great deal of
pain in my ovarian region. It was a cramping kind of pain and
seemed especially severe in the middle of the day. I hadn't yet
learned about ginger compresses and simple home remedies.
Arthur said I needed an azuki bean fast. So I ate a small
bowl of azuki beans with a little gomashio for three days.
While the pain subsided, so did my energy.

Before leaving for California, he made other recommendations on which I didn't fare so well—heavy baked corn
bread for one. He also taught me how to prepare a raw rice
drink with herbs such as gota cola, ginseng, and some other
things that were supposed to be good for the brain. These
were "balanced" with cherry juice concentrates and similar
flavorings. Soon I developed flu-like symptoms in the middle

of the summer. I'd been coughing for several days, and it was funny, because I was trying to tell classmates about my wonderful new diet, but when I'd start talking about it, I was always coughing or blowing my nose, so they weren't all that impressed. Finally, wracked with fever, aches, and periodic chills, I was able to locate Arthur by phone and tell him about my symptoms. He recommended that I get some raw pineapple and crush it and mix it with some of the juice and drink as much as I wanted for a day or two. I did as he said that afternoon, and the next morning woke up free from pain.

Arthur also told me I had excess protein and needed some special drinks. One thing he recommended was frozen orange juice concentrate. He said it would release the old protein and stop the pulling underneath the eyes. I was supposed to eat about a half to one small carton of this per day. He also showed me a drink the Queen of England supposedly made to make her pretty. It contained barley simmered with fresh orange juice and some of the peel. At that time I was unaware of the effects of citrus juices on the body and didn't relate what I was eating to my immediate feelings or my feelings the following day.

Arthur told me a lot about yin and yang, not only as it pertained to food but also to relationships and the world at large. I thought he had infinite wisdom and yet was humble. He had practiced macrobiotics essentially alone for ten years and brought his children up to be macrobiotic by himself, supporting them at the same time. I had a great deal of respect for him. Only much later did I realize he was given to extremes and that his recommendations were unnecessary and, in fact, dangerous. However, had I not weakened my condition with so many yin foods, I would have been intuitive enough not to have taken his advice, and these problems wouldn't have arisen.

I made other mistakes too. Like many beginners, I didn't know how to make balance for the changing seasons. In the summer, I continued to make pressure-cooked brown rice almost every day. I also made roasted and baked rice according to Cornellia's recipe. And all the rice I cooked was the same: short-grain. In fall and winter, this type of cooking and this kind of rice is appropriate, even in Texas. But in spring and summer, and especially in a hot climate, it is important to lighten up. Some rice can be pressure-cooked, but boiling is often more suitable. Instead of short-grain, medium- or long-grain or some combination of different rices is preferred.

East of Eden

Arthur never stayed more than a few days before he left to return to his children in Houston. I, too, longed to leave Dallas. I had taken a few cooking classes in Denton, and there wasn't anyone else in North Texas to study with. I wanted to learn how to make tempeh, pickles, and other macrobiotic foods at home. I wanted to study with experienced cooks and be around macrobiotic friends. I heard about Moniteau Farm, a macrobiotic community in Missouri. They ran notices in *East West Journal* inviting new people to join their rural homestead and take part in their programs. It sounded just like what I needed. I had experienced a lot of pain and heartbreak in the last few years. As I wrote in my journal, "I wonder what God wants with me . . . Let's get on with it . . . Just pour all this misery on [me] because I know a secret, 'Everything changes.' "

I wrote to the folks at Moniteau Farm and introduced myself. They wrote back inviting my son and me to come and stay for a month. I was excited. I figured I would now have a real community to study with, improve Jon's condition, and start off on the right foot. I sent them a deposit and would pay the remaining $350 to cover my room, board, and tuition and started to pack. I had never been away with Jon for so long before and ended filling my car full of clothes, sleeping bags, toys and games, and food for the journey. I had a big Chevy Caprice. It was sleek, sturdy, dependable, and I loved it.

Just before I left, Arthur came by. He told me that Jon should have some fresh pineapple to counteract the animal protein he had had in the past. It was June and pretty hot, so I bought some pineapple for the trip. On the way out of town, I stopped at Infinity, the local health food store, and bought some shampoo, some bread, and Michio Kushi's new book, *The Book of Do-In*. In my diary, I noted, "I want him to be my teacher."

In Oklahoma, I stopped at my brother Hoke's house. I explained to him about macrobiotics and my dream of healing my son with simple country living. I asked him if he thought it was all right to leave my teaching job, pick up, and move so far away from home. "You're a Fields," he told me. "You do what you have to do."

By the time we arrived at Moniteau Farm, Jon was already half sick from eating the pineapple, and he'd been throwing up and couldn't keep anything in his stomach. The people there were eating watermelon. Even though it was early June and warm, I had not been eating very much fruit. I had some watermelon and got diarrhea.

Moniteau Farm was a farm in name only. There was no real farm house, no barn, no fields, no garden, no programs. It consisted of two couples, maybe a half dozen kids, and assorted stragglers, mostly young men who came by for a day or two and moved on. The couples, including the one I had written to, explained that they were in the process of moving onto new property they had just bought. They said the conditions were temporarily a little primitive but would soon change. A lot of the joy of being macrobiotic, they assured me, was being self-reliant and harmonizing with nature.

I had lived in the city so long, I thought there must be something to this. Like the diet I had eaten for years, the comforts and conveniences of modern life weren't natural or healthy. Hard work, exposure to the elements, and cooperating with other people would do Jon and me a world of good.

My son and I initially stayed in an old house with one of the couples and their children. The mother cooked in the mornings and evenings and didn't seem to want any help. Jon and I would steal into the kitchen and get a bite to eat about midday. The food was good—she made blueberry pancakes and freshly baked sourdough bread, miso soups, seaweed dishes, and whole grains. It was like a feast. But she didn't seem happy and had a screaming fight with her husband one night, which left everyone tense. Then it was decided that we would move to the "farm" with the other couple in their small trailer house. We slept on the floor in the front room. However, we couldn't go to sleep until very late because everyone was walking over us. There was no water or electricity, but I didn't mind. That hadn't stopped my ancestors and pioneers in the past. There was a well down the hill, and I'd take the dishes down and wash them. We bathed there too. The trailer didn't have a step to the front door, so Jon couldn't get in and out by himself. The other children were dirty, crying, and hungry. I picked up one of the little girls once and rocked her to sleep, but the mother soon came over and took her away from me. It was clear she didn't like me holding the child.

I soon discovered there were no classes or programs of any kind. No one showed me how to prepare a single dish. The closest thing was on Father's Day when we had pizza for supper. It was made with whole wheat crust and included green beans, green pepper, celery, onions, mushrooms, and sunflower seeds. There was also a dessert made of cantaloupe, raisins, and kuzu. Once when I got diarrhea, someone showed me how to make kuzu tea to stop it.

Nice meals and helpful hints like these were few and far between. Mornings, I'd get my car keys and take Jon to the closest town. There we'd walk around the park and live out of the car till suppertime. Or sometimes we'd take their clothes into the laundry and wash them. Jon continued to have diarrhea.

I kept washing and changing his clothes at the well. His little pants were continually soiled. He was also hyperactive and very hard to drive with. My nerves were shot. One day I got so frustrated I started screaming while coming back from the park.

And the food in the trailer was repetitive—bulgur and steamed bok choy and not much brown rice. The men were working hard physically and always hungry. The only other woman who lived there had a two-week-old baby and spent most of her time resting in the bedroom with the infant. She didn't mind me washing or cleaning the house but drew the line at my being in the kitchen helping with food preparation. One night, we returned from our errands in town and there was no food cooked, so I felt it was time for us to bow out.

I got Jon, collected my things, and left. I didn't know the roads well but we somehow found our way to a place that had gas, a restaurant, and a small motel. We had been there less than a week. Jon saw that there was a bathtub and for the first time in his life, begged to take a bath. He was ecstatic to see running water. We ate dinner at the restaurant. It wasn't organic or natural, but it was served in a calm, peaceful environment.

The trip to Moniteau Farm taught me a lot about human nature and building a new world. Utopia was not just around the corner, at least not the version being created in Missouri. In later years, I heard Moniteau Farm succeeded. They run a bed and breakfast place called Spiral Inn and have visitors from around the country. I wish them well. If I had been more centered, perhaps Jon and I would be living there now.

But at the time, it was a nightmare. On the positive side, I came back from my trip grateful for other things. In the park, I had a chance to read some of Michio's writings, especially on man/woman relations. In my notebook, I jotted down the main points:

1. Diet: for woman, entirely vegetable quality. For man, occasional strong yang (animal food or root vegetables).

2. Man should see that woman is relaxed and secure by preparing a peaceful environment, being considerate, and maintaining harmonious day-to-day interchange. Then woman can relax and be totally responsive to man's initiative.

3. Couples should do more things separately so polarity can be maintained.

4. We should not continually expose ourselves completely (physically).

5. Children, a shared dream, represent mutual understanding and affection and can replace the magnetism of waning physical love.

6. Difficulties help solidify a marriage. You can overcome them by putting special effort into sharing the same dream and working together to achieve it.

Physical love must broaden into social and ideological love— difficulties provide the impetus for this growth.

7. When you tell someone you love them, it means they inspire you and provide you with the incentive to fulfill your nature. It is an admission that you draw strength from him or her. When you love someone you begin to think and speak of *forever*. If you make promises of this nature, they should not be broken.

When we express our love, there can be no conditions. We must not ask them to continue to behave one way or to ask them to change. By making demands, our love becomes negative and cannot last! We should intuitively sense what the other person wants or needs and happily, unconsciously, adapt. Sensitivity is essential.

I also started reading the *Tao Te Ching*. I had heard of Lao Tzu, the ancient Chinese sage, and appreciated the simplicity of his writings. I copied out several passages:

Things which go together naturally do not have to be tied; for they will not separate even without bonds.

To talk little is natural.

There is no greater evil than desiring to change others—

(to take from or give to others what they do not, of their own accord, want to give or take.)

There is no greater misfortune than desiring to change oneself —being discontented with one's lot.

Guiding by example rather than by words or commands is best.

That which is most yielding eventually overcomes what is most resistant.

Vision Quest

On the subject of traveling, Lao Tzu had written that we can learn all we need to know without leaving our homes, but like so many things I didn't follow his advice. My next trip and adventure out of Dallas was not so far—only seventy miles, instead of seven hundred. Later that summer I heard about a woman from Arizona who was leading a vision quest. She had an Indian background and considered herself something of a shamaness. She was going to lead a small group of seekers experience a higher level of awareness.

Except for the trip to Missouri, I had never been out of town since becoming macrobiotic. I was concerned about eating well and packed a big bag of corn bread, rice balls, bancha tea, and different things to take with me. I arranged for Jon to stay with his dad.

The vision quest was taking place in East Texas on some land in the country that someone had donated for this purpose. I was one of about fifteen people who signed up. There were other teachers and professionals like myself, including a psychiatrist who had come all the way from California. And there were non-professionals, a good mixture of different types, ages, and backgrounds.

Friday, the first night, everyone introduced themselves and we bedded down in sleeping bags under the stars. The next day, the Indian woman led us in different activities. We played different games on the grass and engaged in various exercises to expand our individual and group awareness.

The big event of the night was a campfire. Everybody gathered around it and danced. Many people had brought instruments such as drums, flutes, and mariachi rattles. Everyone moved and shaked to the music as they liked. There was no effort to do the same thing. It was good exercise and campfires and starry nights are always magical. One by one people dropped out as they got tired. Those who chose to stayed up all night. I quit before midnight and went back to the main house to rest. But there was so much noise it was impossible to sleep.

The next morning there were still some people dancing. Many of the participants, including the leader, came back to the house in various stages of undress. They also took showers in the open. I was surprised. This was not the kind of experience I had came for. I recalled Michio's fourth point: "We should not continually expose ourselves completely (physically)." Those who go around naked are too yang. They eat too much animal food.

I found a bag of apples and stewed some for breakfast. They were a real hit. The day before I had helped make lentil soup. Some of the other people were aware of natural foods, but I was the only one who really made a practice of it.

Meanwhile, on account of my eating habits, I had unwittingly gotten in trouble. The opening night the leader had laid out the ground rules and explained that alcohol and drugs were not permitted. I kept my bancha tea in a jar inside a small brown paper bag. I carried it with me wherever I went and occasionally took a sip of tea. As the day grew warmer, I drank from the brown bag more frequently. I guess she must have thought I had bourbon in there, which is roughly the same color as bancha. Anyway, word must have gotten around that I was hitting the bottle. I felt the group was standoffish. There were repeated warnings to the group to avoid drinking liquor. Finally, I became comfortable enough to bring the tea and some of the other foods out in the open and the leader later came up to me and laughed and hugged me. Then we all talked and laughed more, and I began to feel much better.

The last afternoon, we gathered again in a circle. The leader asked everyone to tell what the experience meant to them and to contribute and receive a gift. I didn't have anything to give. I didn't wear jewelry. I had no extra clothes. I couldn't think of anything. The only thing I had with me was Michio's *The Book of Macrobiotics*.

Everybody put their present in the middle of the circle. There were lots of pretty earrings, rings, and necklaces. Also pretty scarves, handkerchiefs, and blouses. We went around in a circle and everyone picked a gift. My book was the last one left. I could see that it didn't have the same appeal to them that it had had to me and was puzzled. These were well educated people. I had talked to many of them about macrobiotics, and surely they could find something of value in it.

Sensing my feelings, the leader said, "The giver and the gift are one."

Then a woman came into the circle and picked up my book. I felt elated. Later she invited me to an activity at her home. Whether she was influenced by macrobiotics I don't know, but I felt the spirit of the book and I were somehow united.

I came away from the experience with other insights. The greatest was that for someone to have a spiritual vision they must ask for it not only for themselves but for all mankind.

One of the activities we had done during the weekend was to break up and walk around in any direction for about a half hour. The leader told us to just stop thinking and let the spirit guide us. Then we came back to the circle and described what we had experienced. From my description, the Indian woman told me that I had gone north. North was the direction of ice, cold, and snow-topped mountains. It was where the gods lived and the deepest wisdom. I asked her what this meant for me. She told me I was destined to travel north and learn many things.

8.

Yin and What?

All allemande left to an Alamo style,
Right to your partner and balance awhile.

I HAD BEEN WRITING TO TWO OTHER MEN on Cornellia
Aihara's matchmaking list. The first one was living to
the north of me, in Canada, and we exchanged tape
cassettes. He came down Christmas, and we became engaged
the same day. I had moved into a new home about six months
before and had furnished it nicely and put up Christmas
decorations and had the fireplace cleaned out so all was set
for a blissful holiday. But I grew weary from being in the
kitchen all the time preparing his meals while he did yoga
and relaxed, and he grew upset over my son's hyperactivity
and chattering on a trip to visit my family. Then there was
the question of where we would live. From the stories I'd
heard of Canada's temperatures, I wasn't anxious to move
there, and he couldn't see leaving his native land, and there
was the question of how Jon's visits to his father would be
arranged. All in all there seemed to be more difficulties than
advantages, so we soon broke up.

The other one, Harlan, lived in Southern California and
worked for the railroad as a flagman. He always enclosed
beautiful photographs and wrote of many exciting activities—
mountain climbing, going to balloon festivals and riding in
balloons, and going to the macrobiotic summer camp at
French Meadows. And he'd send me wonderful recipes of
pickles and bread. He had studied with Jacques de Langre and
was into bread making. He gave me encouragement with the
diet, and I looked forward to seeing the brightly colored

envelopes he sent sticking out of the mailbox. He made me realize that there was a world outside the work-a-day world of worry and unhappiness that I'd known, and there were beautiful places to see and interesting people to meet. I might never have left the security of job and home in Texas if it had not been for Harlan.

Our friendship continued to grow and in January, 1980, I went to visit him. He took me to see the boats on the ocean and to dinner at a beautiful restaurant in the mountains over-looking the bay and to quaint little shops that specialized in Indian relics and spiritual momentos. He introduced me to his friends, took me to macrobiotic restaurants, and showed me the big Erewhon store in Los Angeles. I thought I was in heaven.

I felt a little out of place with my $200 sheepskin coat, but I'd leave it in the car when we went out with these people who had no furniture, just throw pillows to sit on. They had wonderful kitchens and many tools I'd never seen before—cutting boards, grain mills, Oriental chopping knives, and lovely straw baskets filled with fresh vegetables. And one woman prepared the most delicious meals. It was clear they were rich in ways that I wasn't.

Harlan asked me to marry him, and I saw in him the possibility of family unity. With him working outside and me in the home cooking, I could take care of my son and possibly improve his health through macrobiotics. Jon was in nursery school, and in Texas it was hard to take care of him and handle my job responsibly at the same time. When he was sick, I'd take off work and stay home with him. Also there was a lot of tension with my ex-husband. Joe couldn't see why I didn't give Jon some of the foods he was accustomed to. I kept a little cheese and bread in the house but drew the line at meat. Even my sister Dot, who came to visit with her grandchildren, thought it was awful when I refused to let Jon have a hamburger with the other kids at a local drive-in restaurant. I thought a more sympathetic environment would make it easier for both of us to eat well.

When I returned to Irving, coaxed by Harlan's daily telephone calls, I decided to move to California. I had some reservations since he'd never met my son, but I was so attracted to him and the idea of having my family together that I made plans to leave. Compared to Texas, the natural foods community in California was thriving. In Denton and Dallas, I often drove 100 miles round trip to get my weekly groceries.

Meanwhile, my financial situation had improved. Following the divorce, I made some money in real estate, bought a three-bedroom brick house in Irving for myself and my son, and invested the rest in silver and gold. It was a time of high inflation, and the value of precious metals went soaring.

After deciding to move to California, I quit my job with the schools and sold most of my things, including the washer and dryer. I also traded my color television for a dilapidated black and white model. I was concerned that the artificial electromagnetic radiation from the color set might be unhealthy.

At the end of January, I shipped my remaining furniture and moved out to California. However, things didn't go as expected. Jon missed his dad and grandmother a lot and because of his insecurity needed constant attention from me. Harlan assured me before that he would be a good step-father, but he couldn't cope with Jon's special needs. Essentially, Harlan was too yang. He went to work at all hours. He left the house at 4:30 A.M. on some days and returned at that time on other ones. He worked several days on and then several days off. Although he said he could support us, he actually had very little income. We lived mostly on what I had brought. In a few short months, we went through a good deal of my savings, including a couple of thousand to fix his car which he had totaled.

The apartment we lived in was located in a hilly area of the city. There was a series of stairs built into the hillside leading up the house from the streets below. Harlan would make Jon walk the stairs for exercise. I could hardly climb them myself, and Jon had a hard time walking, much less climbing. He also spanked Jon for writing on the calendar. My son had seen him writing at his desk and thought he'd do it too. I didn't say much the first time. I thought kids sometimes needed to be disciplined. But the next time Jon marked his calendar and Harlan started to spank him, I said no. I explained to him that Jon didn't intentionally disobey. He hadn't understood what he wasn't supposed to do or didn't remember. Harlan whipped him anyway. That really upset me, and I started bawling, too.

In the kitchen, I found it difficult to fix food for Harlan to take to work at all hours of the day and night, to pack a lunchbox for Jon to take to kindergarten, and to learn to cook myself. Like many people who had come to macrobiotics through reading George Ohsawa's books or studying with teachers in California, Harlan was very rigid. His diet was extremely salty. He baked bread with too much salt in it and loved to make bran pickles. I was always craving something yin. But he didn't want me to have a single salad, piece of fruit, or other raw food. He said he wouldn't tolerate them in the house. I came to regard one small fresh leaf of watercress in the soup as a sinful treat. Harlan was also into herbs and made strange concoctions to bring us into balance. One containing yellow dock and kombu was supposed to cleanse the liver. God knows we needed it.

One day I went to church and came home to find that Jon had fallen down the patio steps and hit his head. It was bleeding. He had been sitting in a cardboard box on the steps, and the box had naturally toppled. Harlan had promised to watch him but obviously hadn't. The proverbial final straw came soon after when Harlan went off to a party by himself and then over to an old girlfriend's house. Feeling anxious, I phoned and asked him to come home. He didn't. I packed up my car that night.

Santa Fe

I left all my beautiful furniture and almost everything behind
except the silver and gold. After selling my property in
Texas, I invested all my money in silver and gold bars. I was
waiting for the economy to crash. I didn't trust the banks.
But the only thing that crashed was me. I took what cooking
utensils and clothes I could carry in the back of the Chevy.
I put a small futon in the back seat for Jon, and we took off
in the heavy Los Angeles traffic, heading east.

Earlier, I had picked Santa Fe, New Mexico, off the map
as a place I would move to when I left California. I was
embarrassed to return to Texas after telling all my friends I
was leaving to get married. Santa Fe was about half way
between L.A. and Dallas. It was a long drive, 900 miles.
Santa Fe turned out to be very beautiful, and Jon and I ended
up staying there for over a year.

Santa Fe was an unusual place. A traditional healing center
settled by the Indians, it had been home to the Spaniards for
several centuries before the arrival of English-speaking home-
steaders, ranchers, and prospectors. About fifty years ago it
became a famous art colony, and painters like Georgia
O'Keeffe lived in the surrounding desert. Many of the homes
were made of adobe, and the city was still proud of its Indian
and Old World heritage. In recent years, it has become somewhat of a mecca for the holistic community. Many young
men and women seeking spiritual enlightenment were drawn
here for one reason or another. I noticed many of them were
yin. The men tended to have long hair and voices like women.

There were two massage schools, a College of Natural
Medicine, an acupuncture school, herb shops that compared to
those in the largest of cities, and a large natural foods co-op.
There was also some macrobiotic activity. In the early '70s,
Jack Garvy, an editor of *East West Journal*, and his wife,
Barbara Benker, had come out from Boston to start a rural
community in Arizona. However, they split up, and the

community never really developed. Jack went back East, and Barbara was now sharing her life with someone else, and together they started up a macrobiotic restaurant about two blocks from my house.

The city was a popular vacation spot and doubled or tripled in population in the summer. Everyone told me it would be impossible to find a reasonable place to stay. But I didn't stop hoping. One day I was looking through the rental section and saw an ad for a small adobe house for rent. We went over to see it and loved it at first sight. It had hardwood floors and a peaceful vibration. The manager was vegetarian, and there was a feeling of harmony between us from the beginning. We moved in after letting go the trailer house we stayed in on first arriving.

Santa Fe was a wonderful place to be. I thrived on the intellectual and cultural ferment, although I didn't feel any urgency to study other approaches and techniques. As I noted in my diary, "I've rushed around and studied almost all my life looking for that ultimate insight or ultimate way—but now I don't feel as if I have to struggle anymore. The eyeglasses of yin-yang and the macrobiotic diet seem to be enough. I still study at home a lot—but I am content to meditate, eat well, and listen to my own body-mind for guidance. I do need to learn patience—patience in waiting for answers sometimes and patience in changing my condition."

The climate and weather in New Mexico were very different from Texas. Santa Fe was high up, 7,000 feet, and surrounded by mountains in every direction. In the winter it snowed but warmed up during the day. Sometimes it was unbelievably snowy. It was hard to tell where the mountains ended and the sky began as everything was one big blanket of white. We didn't socialize much that year. It was hard to get a sitter, and I never really felt comfortable leaving Jon and going out. It felt unnatural. But on Christmas Eve, Jon and I went to a chant and pot luck and then to another macrobiotic friend's home for desserts. The people were so warm and friendly. I felt as if I was with family, although this was the first Christmas I'd ever been away from relatives.

At the party, I met many interesting people. There was a man studying acupuncture. His teacher, Sensei Nakazone, was from Japan and had studied in France with George Ohsawa at one time. He recommended a diet similar to macrobiotics but allowed 20 percent animal foods, especially fish and chicken. Then there was an acupuncturist who moved down recently from Illinois. He seemed real clear and provided a good service. One of the local macrobiotic men had just returned from Holland where he had been witnessing for the Hopi Indians in some of their legal struggles. Then I met a macrobiotic couple who'd recently moved down from Boston, a woman who worked for the co-op, and another who made and sold seitan. The woman who made seitan was named Irene Swain. I took some cooking classes with her. There was one whole class on desserts, and I learned how to make a parsnip cake without flour.

I also became friends with Rita Solice who lived nearby. One day a little boy came over. He said his mother wanted to know if we had any bread she could borrow. I was very self-conscious about my natural foods diet. I figured she was used to ordinary white bread and wouldn't want any of our hard, dark brown bread. I told the boy, "I don't think she would like it. It's not the kind you find at the store."

He came back in a little while. He said, "My mother wants the bread." I'd forgotten what poor was. I realized they had nothing to eat and readily let him have it. Later I got to know Rita. From time to time, I'd give her a little food or money. She would always pay the money back. Then she'd watch Jon some when I went to town.

In Santa Fe, I decided not to work but to devote the rest of the year to caring and cooking for my son. For lunch I would send him to school with tempeh, some brown rice, cooked vegetables or beans, soup in a little container, and sometimes some fruit. He did pretty well. Sometimes the other

kids felt sorry for him and would give him a roll. After
school Jon would come home on the bus and the first thing
he'd say as he came in the door was "I'm hungry!" I'd fix
him something to eat. He was beginning to appreciate the
food.

I still had some health problems of my own in Santa Fe.
My lungs were weak and I cried a lot. Jon needed constant
attention when he was at home. He needed help dressing and
bathing and even getting a drink of water. I was under a lot
of pressure. I invited his teachers over for dinner, told them
about macrobiotics and what we were trying to accomplish by
following this way of life, and asked for their help. But they
didn't sympathize or understand. Soon after I got a request to
send money for him to buy ice cream, and his stainless steel
food containers were mysteriously lost on picnics and outings.
When school let out for the summer, I let Jon visit his father.
Jon had been back to Irving for one week during spring break
and then again during the Christmas holidays. When he came
back, he was flushed and more hyper than usual and craved
grapefruit juice. I was taking some occasionally myself, so
I let him have as much as he wanted, and he soon got sick.
Often he'd be sick for several days. At these times I'd call
some of the macrobiotic people in Santa Fe, but they weren't
very helpful. One said it's often best to do nothing. Irene
kept telling me to widen the diet, but I didn't think that was
a good idea. I wrote to Herman Aihara, the senior macrobiotic teacher on the West Coast. I heard that he did consultations by mail. He replied that he needed more information.
I sent him some more material. He said that our situation
was "very deep and sad" and would take many years to
improve.

Journey to Boston

In the *East West Journal,* I saw an announcement for a five-
week intensive at the Kushi Institute and sent away for a

brochure. The session included lectures by Michio and cooking classes with Aveline. I wanted to practice macrobiotics properly, learn why I wasn't feeling well, and help my son. I wrote to Boston and asked about coming up to study and whether there was somewhere we could stay. The person who got my letter at the K.I. was from Denton! I had attended a class she gave on cooking tempura. She wrote back, referring me to a macrobiotic study house in Brookline that might take a child. I called and made arrangements for us to stay there so I could attend Level I.

There were no direct flights to Boston. We had to take a bus to Albuquerque and then fly to Dallas and change planes. On the way, I kept dreaming of all the wonderful food that would be awaiting us. The house we were staying at was located across from the high school on Davis Street in Brookline Village. The woman who ran it was named Cathy.

We left Santa Fe early in the morning, but it was early evening before we got Boston, and there was nothing left from dinner except a pan of corn bread. It was nothing like the rich, delicious corn bread we was used to in Texas and New Mexico. And worst of all, it was cold. But still we were grateful. The minute we arrived, Cathy sat us down and told us the rules of the house. She explained what we could and could not do. Jon and I were so hungry, and except for a slender futon our room was bare. There was not even a chest of drawers or hangers for our clothes. By the end of our first day there, we wanted to go home.

Life in the study house remained spartan. I paid Cathy and her husband $700 a month for room and board, plus extra for child care for Jon while I attended classes. Even then, I seldom had breakfast or lunch there, and she didn't cook on weekends. In time we were allowed to use the kitchen ourselves to cook.

As a city, Boston was very pretty. It was the first time I had ever been in the North. I liked the large trees. They were so much fuller than the trees in Texas. Also the homes in New England were much older. In some cases, they had been built several centuries ago. When I was selling real estate in Dallas, houses built only twenty-five years were considered hard to market. People in the Southwest didn't want to live in anything more than seven or eight years old. I didn't value the older homes in Texas as much then either. They seemed so different.

Another difference was that most of the houses in Boston were two or three stories high. In Texas they were mostly one story. I wasn't used to climbing stairs and found it tiring. The study house was on the third floor of an old Victorian walk-up. Jon had a hard time climbing. He took stairs very slowly, one at a time. Just to go in and out of the house was a major effort.

Although I had lived in Texas for most of my life, I never got used to the heat. I had been looking forward to spending a cool summer up North. To my surprise, the heat and humidity in Boston were awful. At least in Texas, the heat is dry. Here it was humid. Our clothes got sopping wet. The apartment didn't have air conditioning, and there was only one fan which we shared during the day but not at night. Jon and I were constantly drenched in sweat and changed clothes two to three times a day.

Washing our things took a lot of time and energy. Cathy had a washing machine, but I wasn't allowed to use it. Just to get the clothes done was like a military mobilization. I'd have to get a cab (which wasn't always easy), carry the clothes down three flights of stairs, go to the laundromat, get a cab back, and go up the stairs—all with Jon in tow. I ended up washing them by hand every day as much as I could. Meanwhile, Cathy and the other woman staying in the house were washing clothes every day in the washer. One day when Cathy was away, I asked the other woman if I could put a skirt or pair of Jon's shorts in with her clothes. She said no.

I'd heard people in the North were cold, but I was unprepared for the frostiness I experienced on my arrival. During my stay, I didn't really make friends with any Northern women, though some from the Midwest and South were very friendly. Perhaps this was just a basic yin/yang difference. Because of the colder climate and stronger diet, including more animal food, Northerners were more yang—active and abrupt. They were always busy and had little time to talk. On account of their warmer climate and lighter meals, including less animal food, Southerners were more yin—relaxed, polite, and talkative.

Cathy sometimes socialized with other women. Instead of feeling hurt by her neglect and waiting to be included, I could have been more assertive. Back in Texas my friend Gwen had told me that when she came to Boston, the people were always hurrying her up. She got so yang eating the food, she started binging on ice cream. I didn't believe her until I saw it for myself.

On the positive side, I noticed that Cathy and her husband never lost their temper or said anything unkind to each other. It was a marvel I attributed to their way of eating. Also they were extremely kind to Jon, taking him to a Red Sox baseball game, and I appreciated that.

When classes started, I felt more comfortable. The Kushi Institute was located in a reconverted mop factory in Brookline Village. There were two big classrooms on the third floor and counseling offices, a small classroom, and a big kitchen with cast-iron stoves on the second floor. The *East West Journal* was also located in the same building as were several artists studios. The T, or trolley, to Boston ran along Station Street, across the street.

Brookline Village was an older part of town with small stores and shops as well as town hall, police and fire headquarters, and the main library. There was also a post office, several antique shops, three florists, a fish market, a stationery store, and several bookshops. People in the village knew each other, and in that respect it was closer to a small town back home than a typical Boston neighborhood or suburb where people hardly knew their neighbors.

After the K.I. opened and the East West Foundation moved from Boston to Brookline, other macrobiotic activities developed in the Village. Erewhon's Village Natural Foods Store and Horai-San Macrobiotic Book and Cookware Store were located on Washington St., around the corner from the Kushi Institute. Open Sesame Macrobiotic Restaurant did a thriving business a minute's walk across Route 9, though almost as many macrobiotic friends could be found, having coffee in Abe and Marsha's Deli up the street.

I arrived late at the K.I. for orientation. They were introducing the teachers, and I heard a man talking about Aikido. He said it was good for the development of the mind. It developed the power of concentration. "That's for me!" I thought. "I'll sign up. I want to develop my mind."

The Aikido studio was located at 17 Station Street next to one of the K.I. classrooms. I didn't know Aikido was a martial art and when I went in discovered people getting creamed. I couldn't see what relationship getting thrown down to the floor had to the mind. I saw that to survive you had to concentrate, but that seemed a strange way to develop mental awareness. Later on, I learned that energy could be directed to different areas, but by then I was too sore and tired to continue.

The first day of Aikido was an experience I'll never forget. I had always backed away from exercises that were too physically demanding or too masculine. Two hours of being dropped, rolled, thrown, and stretched were excruciating, but the moment of glory came when I pinned someone else to the ground. For a single instant, I was in total command of myself and my world. As I jotted down in my diary, "Even my thoughts of romance pale in the dream of studying Aikido."

One day I arrived late (no doubt on account of my Southern, slower, more yin background) and heard Bill Gleason,

the instructor, talking about different levels of physical
strength. He mentioned someone with no strength at all. I
looked around, studying the others, trying to figure out who
he was talking about. Of course it was me, but I didn't know
it until later. Bill was very gentle with me during practice,
but I felt I was behind everyone else. But mostly, I already
had too much physical activity to stay. I was walking to and
from classes two or three times a day, going up and down
stairs, taking Jon with me sometimes, plus doing shiatsu and
do-in. I dropped out after two weeks. It's better not to be
involved in too many activities at one time, beneficial as
they are.

One of my favorite teachers at the Kushi Institute was Ed
Esko. He was very knowledgeable, clear, and stimulating. He
taught the Order of the Universe and devoted the term to
discussing astronomy and other sciences. He also introduced
me to Nine Star Ki, a system of Oriental thought that can
be used to understand your character, destiny, and relationships with other people. I loved Nine Star Ki and could hardly
wait to get to Ed's classes.

I also enjoyed Bill Tims, though he lectured to our group
only occasionally. He was a native Oklahoman, a fellow
Southwesterner, and I loved to hear the way he talked as
much as what he said. He taught visual diagnosis. He was
always dividing the class up into groups and asking us to
classify each other according to size, shape, constitution, and
condition. One time he asked us to decide who was the most
yang. I had always had the impression that yang was it—
healthy, active, strong, happy, alive. The worst thing you
could say to another macrobiotic person was that they were
too yin—unhealthy, passive, weak, unhappy, dead. Or at
least that's what I thought then.

In my group, there were two other women besides myself
who claimed they were the most yang. We got into a royal
argument, and my liver really started to show up. One of the
women was stockier than I and had shorter hair. On the
other hand, I had been raised with many brothers and by only

one parent—both extreme yang factors. As it turned out, we were all too yang and repelled each other.

Later I learned that Michio Kushi's use of yin and yang was different from George Ohsawa's. Where Ohsawa held up yang as ideal and denigrated yin, Michio felt that they were complementary and that we needed a balance of each. In most practical situations, Michio also leaned toward Lao Tzu's view that yin was superior to yang and that we are more apt to realize our goals by yielding and grateful acceptance than by force and argument.

I also enjoyed the cooking classes at the K.I. They were given mainly by Wendy Esko, Ed's wife. She fixed a chow mein dish that was unforgettable. She also prepared the most delicious seitan stew I'd ever tasted. I also took a medicinal cooking class from Aveline Kushi. She taught us how to make brown rice cream, an azuki-kombu-squash dish, and Corsican tea. Aveline always had several young women assisting her. Olivia Oredson, director of the cooking program, was also very warm and helpful.

The cooking classes were a great help to me, though I couldn't always figure out what was going in what pot. There were so many dishes being fixed at one time, it was hard to keep them straight. Also the kitchen was small, and there was usually a crowd around the cook so it was hard to see. To remedy this, big mirrors had been placed overhead. But learning to cook in a mirror is not the easiest thing, and I was always confusing the right and left hand. Despite these handicaps, I was elated. There were then very few macrobiotic cookbooks to learn from. Wendy's first one had just come out. Lima Ohsawa and Cornellia Aihara's cookbooks were nice but too Oriental for everyday use.

One of the highlights of my day was eating breakfast at Open Sesame. I'd eat before class and have miso soup and a bowl of oatmeal or soft rice. Sometimes I would take Jon with me. Other times he stayed at the apartment and ate later with the other children. We also went to the Seventh Inn downtown and Sanae on Newbury Street. Sanae was more informal, and Jon loved to wander around from table to table talking with people. People were attracted to our Southern drawl. They'd ask him all sorts of questions, and he would tell them whatever they asked—where we were from, how old I was, and so on.

With classes, attending to Jon, and doing the laundry, I didn't have time for much socializing. Once with Cathy I went to Bo-In Lee's house. He was a Buddhist yoga teacher from Korea. He had a son about Jon's age, and they enjoyed playing together. I had a consultation with him about Jon. He recommended some postures and corrective exercises. As in some of the body work classes I'd tried in Dallas, he felt that by releasing physical blockages corresponding emotional and mental blockages could be reduced. I tried some of his exercises, but they took more than one person to do with Jon and I gave up. I also attended one of Bo-In Lee's weekend retreats in New Hampshire or western Massachusetts. Jon and I rode up with Dr. Anthony Satillaro, a medical doctor who had relieved his own cancer with the help of macrobiotics. He later wrote a best-selling book on his experience.

Three weeks into the program, I met Bob Mattson at a dance at the K.I. He was a native of Boston and very friendly, concerned, and caring. He took me rollerskating in the park and Jon and me to the beach.

Another time Bob took us somewhere that looked out over the harbor and told us how the land had been filled in and about various other events that gave me the feel of Boston's history. He also brought us home to his place in Cambridge and cooked dinner. That was very nice. Just before I went back to New Mexico, he asked me why I didn't come and stay in Boston. I told him it was difficult finding a study house or place to stay that accepted children and that I'd already moved twice that year. We later corresponded, and I told him he was too yin. In many ways I was still too yang.

Bob gave me notes of some of Michio's old lectures.

Listening to him talk in person was always a joy. Once Michio gave a lecture on children, and a lot of people in the community attended. He talked about how modern people had degenerated by no longer eating whole cereal grains as the center of their diet.

Michio seemed to know what was going through our minds. He laughed and said not to worry or feel gulty. Whatever we had made, we could unmake. Through proper eating and way of life, almost any condition or illness could be reversed.

Until then I didn't know whether macrobiotics could help Jon or not. I had taken him to so many specialists. We had seen a leading neurologist in Dallas at the Children's Medical Center who could find nothing wrong. In Los Angeles, I took him to a clinical psychologist specializing in developmental problems. She was little help. I also had tried a chiropractor, but nothing had come of the treatment.

Bo-In Lee had recommended that I see Michio for a consultation. I kept calling for an appointment and was told he was booked up for months. I persisted. Finally on the fourteenth call, I was told I could see him for a few minutes after class. I brought Jon, and he fell asleep on the floor during the lecture. I woke him up and took him to Michio. I told him that Jon had difficulty reading and writing and walking, climbing stairs, and running.

Michio looked at Jon for a minute or two. He said he was genetically normal and that his problems resulted from eating too much cheese and eggs when he was little. He said these things had created a mucous condition in the sinuses that was blocking the flow of energy to the meridians which went to the legs—making it difficult for Jon to run, hop, and climb. Also it was the source of his speech difficulties. Meat and dairy food had also caused liver contractions, and this was related to his inability to stay still. Michio recommended a strict diet for Jon: no animal food, no oil, no flour products, no fruit except on very hot days, no juices, and almost no desserts. He could have squash pie without the crust. He also recommended lotus root plasters for about three weeks. He said they would drain out the mucus that was blocking his energy. He felt Jon's symptoms could be relieved after one year of good macrobiotic cooking.

Rod House was another strong influence. An artist, poet, and teacher at the K.I., Rod had been practicing and teaching macrobiotics for many years. I went to him for shiatsu. We had a strong sense of having known each other. His apartment was very neat and orderly.

The treatment was a little painful, but something about his presence made me open up. I told him about some of my problems. I thought of myself as weak. He said, "You may not know how strong you are." He had two altars, one for One Peaceful World and another for family or individuals. I gave him a picture of Jon and me and asked if he'd keep us in his prayers. I also left him a pillow. When I left, I felt like he'd given me so much, yet charged so little. I felt he really cared.

Another positive influence was a Japanese acupuncturist who was living at the Kushis and whose name I can't remember. She was warm and compassionate. I felt "valued" by her as we say in psychology.

My trip to Boston was a great success. Michio's consultation took a big strain off my mind. I was responsible for my son's problems. Now I would be responsible for healing him. I had a fair amount of experience and study preparing macrobiotic food. I could make sushi, noodles, pickles, and amasake. I felt I could go back home.

As the term came to an end, I bought a new pressure-cooker, a Foley's food mill, and other cookware and had them shipped home from Horai-San. I spent lots of money in Boston. I guess it was part of a big discharge I was going through.

As I wrote to a friend,

Boston was an incredible experience, long hours in class and very hot and humid but worth every minute of it. We studied medical cooking under the world's leading teacher. . . . I'm thinking about using this knowledge to open a house or center for children with severe emotional or behavioral problems—the ones that others have given up on. Will see how things go in the next month of two, but I'm praying for guidance now—if that's what God wants me to do, I'm sure doors will open.

9.

An Invisible Cord

Balance forward and balance back
Turn with the right hand half about.

SHORTLY AFTER I GOT BACK FROM BOSTON, Arthur came to
Santa Fe with his son and a friend of his son's and stayed
a week. He had been my first macrobiotic boyfriend, and
I respected his views. He said Michio didn't give me the
right guidelines. He said he just gave me a standard approach
and not one actually suited to Jon's individual needs. Arthur
proceeded to take matters into his own hands and gave Jon
some niacin tablets to calm him down. It was effective in
calming him down, but it would cause his whole body to flush
and turn red. And Jon soon protested so I felt it best to stop.
Although Arthur had almost ten years' more macrobiotic
experience than I had, I knew there was a better way. Still, he
had planted some seeds of doubt. I was confused and didn't
know which way to go.

While the school authorities in Santa Fe arranged for Jon
to be transferred to a special class for children with communication disorders, I started implementing the dietary
recommendations Michio gave me with a few adjustments
suggested by Arthur. I cooked everything we ate from
scratch. We ate no animal food, no chemicals, no preserva-
tives, and no refined salt or sugar. Soon I could see encouraging changes. Jon started reading—at first just large words
on cards that I made for him. But at least he was making the
neurological connections and in time would be able to read
smaller words. He was such a different person. Even the
teachers seemed impressed.

His walking, running, and motor coordination also improved. When we first moved to Santa Fe, I'd take him to the park and he'd run six to nine feet and then stop as if he had imaginary boundaries around him. After coming back from Boston and adjusting his diet, with encouragement he ran around the entire park! He also started playing with the other children. I felt encouraged.

We also did more things together. I took Jon to a balloon festival in Albuquerque. About 300 balloons went up. He loved it. We went to see *Song of the South*, Walt Disney's lovely film about Uncle Remus and Old Brer Rabbit. Jon and I came home and made a sign for our "Laughingest Place" and were in there off and on all day laughing our heads off and acting silly.

One of the things I noticed most was more subtle. I found myself seeing him as a different child. Jon's vibrations were different. He was more pleasant to be around, and his skin began to get so pretty. My own condition seemed to be improving also. My skin was much nicer and my digestion better. I knew both he and I had a long way to go to "perfect" health, but it was so rewarding to see some positive changes at last.

In a letter to a friend back in Boston, I enthused:

> There's a quality to our relationship that didn't exist before —being a mother has taken on a new dimension—difficult to explain. We even laugh together and have fun in the park here. And I'm happier than I've ever been in my whole life . . . just doing the same simple things. Sometimes I get frustrated with the strictness of my routine, but then I let up for a day or two and I'm ready to go again. . . . I'm just so grateful that I have the opportunity to do what I'm doing.

Lotus Root Adventure

Some of Jon's progress came as a result of applying lotus root plasters. Michio had said that as soon as the mucus was

drained out of his sinuses, I would see a lot of changes.
Getting the lotus root and getting Jon to wear the plaster
was a real adventure.

Lotus root wasn't available locally so I wrote Bob Mattson
in Boston who shipped some, but it wasn't enough to last
three weeks. I wrote someone in Los Angeles to look for
some when it came on the market out there. Finally the co-op
in Santa Fe agreed to order some. The minimum order was
a full case, which turned out to be 60 pounds or enough for
the whole neighborhood, and I agreed to pay for whatever
they didn't sell. I gave a workshop on lotus root plasters to
help sell it and had one person show up.

The next hurdle was Jon. To make the plaster, you grate
a handful of lotus root, mix it with a little freshly grated
gingerroot and some flour, and put it on a piece of cheesecloth
or clean cotton. Night after night, I would put the plaster
across Jon's sinuses, forehead, and nose—and mine too—to
open up blockages. Jon would pull it off. I put it on earlier.
He would still pull it off. I told him he could watch TV if he
kept the compress on. It didn't work. He pulled it off.
Whether it was just unfamiliar or uncomfortable, I couldn't get
him to keep the plaster on.

I came to dread doing them. It required so much discipline
to stop everything every evening and prepare the plasters and
stay with him to see that he kept them on. But I felt they
were critical to his future health and happiness. I guess they
did help some. His nose ran for weeks. A lot of mucus came
out, but it didn't pull it out as it should. I knew there was
still a lot of additional buildup from years of eating milk,
cheese, ice cream, refined flour, and other poor quality foods,
but I'd exhausted my sources for getting lotus root and
my patience.

Hope Springs Eternal

The weather heated up that summer, and I had difficulty making the diet yin enough for Jon. He was not supposed to have

194

any raw salads or raw fruits and only stewed fruits occasionally, so he was always begging for yinnie syrup, raisins, or something sweet. Also he wanted grapefruit and grapefruit juice. I didn't use too much salt or miso in our cooking, which is the usual reason macrobiotic people crave sweets, fruit, and juices. I figured maybe we were eating too many grains. I stopped pressure-cooking my rice at every meal and tried to eat it only once a day. Also we were still having some baked foods—bread and cookies and vegetable pies—as I didn't know how to make many flourless desserts. And my cooking wasn't as fresh as it could've been. Boiled and pressed salads were foreign to me so I didn't prepare them often. I was also getting too yang and craving sweets.

As my own condition improved, my longstanding health problems began to ease. Before leaving Texas, I went in for a medical check up. I didn't tell the physician about the earlier diagnosis of masses or tumors on my ovaries. I just mentioned to her that I had had some cysts in the past. She examined me and said that one side was normal and the other had a small cyst. I was elated. Later in Santa Fe, my cousin Cliff Fields, visiting from Houston, encouraged me to get a second opinion. I found another physician. She also gave me a breast and pelvic examination and took a pap smear and gave me a clean bill of health. Thanks to macrobiotics, my breast lumps and ovarian masses were gone. Also I seldom had any menstrual pain since changing my diet to grains and vegetables and my cycle was regular.

In a letter to Carmen, the co-pastor of the Today Church, I reviewed the positive changes in my health. She was still eating raw foods, and I wanted to share with her some of the things I had learned:

To make a long story short, I've been eating grains and following the macrobiotic program to the best of my ability and judgment (which hasn't always been too good) for over two years now, and I am enjoying excellent health and am much stronger than I've ever been in my life. . . .

What I've discovered is that grains *do not have to be* mucus forming, though they can be. Most of us have weakened our intestines with refined foods, saturated fats, and sweets for so many years that our intestines are too weak to transmute a slow-burning energy food such as a whole grain. And most of us have forgotten how to chew. I found that if I added slight amounts of pickle or other fermented food such as sauerkraut at each meal and chewed all grains about 50 times per bite, there was no problem with digestion or mucus. I have eliminated a lot of things from my diet that weaken the intestines such as [raw] fruit, too many liquids, yeasted bread. . . .

I learned at the Today Church to try everything for myself and judge the truth for myself, and that's what I've done.

As I indicated to Carmen, my intuition seemed to improve along with my physical health. At one time Arthur was away in Alaska for several months. We didn't correspond. One day, right in the middle of washing the dishes, I got this hunch to call his father's house in Santa Fe. "This is Gale, a friend of Arthur's. Have you heard from him lately?" I asked. I had never called him before.

"This is Arthur," the voice replied. "I just got back from Alaska. I haven't been in the house more than ten minutes."

As the year wore on, however, I began to lose my center. Both Jon and I got too yang. We ate too many baked flour products. We enjoyed going to the local macrobiotic restaurant. Jon loved the seitan sandwiches, but they were too salty for his condition. He grew very thin. I liked their Tex-Mex special, with enchiladas and beans. They were a little spicy. And my rigorous routine with little socializing was making me tense and often on edge.

Each week I got a massage from a man at the College of Natural Medicine. He usually worked deep in the tissues. It relaxed me, but I didn't have any energy for a couple days afterwards, and Jon would be too much to handle. I began to grow weary of New Mexico. "This is a unique land, but it doesn't feel like home to me," I wrote. "I expect I'll move back to Texas next year."

My social life gradually started to pick up. I became friendly with a woman who had a six-year-old. She wanted to start macrobiotics, and I began teaching her cooking on an informal basis and having her over for dinner. She later moved to Tulsa. My sister Dot and her husband Bob came up to visit. She bought my diamond engagement ring that Joe had given me and that helped us out financially. "It's best to keep it in the family," she explained.

About this time I started attending the Church of Religious Science. It wasn't as dynamic or inspiring as the Today Church, but it had a positive philosophy and fulfilled some of my spiritual needs. "It heals by leading us to the things we need sometimes or from the outside in, while food heals from the inside out. At least that's how I have it figured at the moment," I told a friend.

At church I also started seeing auras for the first time. I had been meditating and practicing eye exercises. One day while looking at the minister, I saw a beautiful white light shining around her. She was dressed in a deep wine color so I know it wasn't a reflection. I had strikingly good vibrations of her already, mainly from her voice. The thrill of seeing a full aura for the first time is indescribable. It was like regaining some forgotten or unused abilities.

While giving a workshop on lotus root plasters, I met another man. His name was Richard. He was born in December—opposite to me— and we became close friends. He was warm, affectionate, and sensitive—all those nice yin things. He was younger than I was, but he came from California and had broad exposure to personal growth activities and was neither sexist nor very concerned about age. In other respects, we were very different. He was Jewish, I was Baptist. With a master's degree in social science, he kept up with everything that went on in the world, while I could hardly keep up with what was going on in my house and cared little about the rest of the world.

Several years before, Richard had smoked pot on a regular basis and had pretty, long hair. He had been vegetarian a long time and had lived with the Sikhs, a dedicated group seeking spiritual enlightenment whose guru was from India. They ate a lot of dairy, including cheese, and garlic, ginger, and onions, as well as fruits and fruit juices. He had read some about macrobiotics but no having his own kitchen was not doing too well. Even though he jogged about a half hour a day, he was still quite yin. He liked eating my cooking and was anxious to leave the Sikh community, so I asked him to move in with Jon and me for awhile.

I began to cook for Richard most of the time. I also give haircuts and offered to do his hair. I was pleased that he asked me to trim it a little shorter each time I cut it. That showed he was getting more yang and returning to balance. For Thanksgiving, Jon and I drove to Pecos to visit my sister and her family. Richard came with us.

Back in Santa Fe, Richard began seeing one of Sensei Nakazone's students for acupuncture treatments. She recommended that he eat more fish and chicken, up to 20 percent. He was also running 5 miles a day. He got tighter and tighter. Jon began getting on his nerves, and he encouraged me to let him go live with his father. I couldn't take Richard's attitude toward my son. It was rubbing off on me and making me resentful. It didn't matter how good a mood we were in, when he would come in things became real tense. To balance the fish and chicken, he began craving fruit and sweets. He wanted to become yang quickly, but I kept telling him slower is sometimes faster after all.

And I, too, was encouraged by one of Nakazone's students to eat chicken and since my energy was low, I decided to try it. But I never felt right about it and found it hard to digest so I soon stopped but Richard continued. But by that time he had his own apartment and was cooking for himself.

Having been unemployed for several months, Richard went

to check out the job situation in Texas. There was an oil boom in the Midland-Odessa area, where I had gone to junior college. But he couldn't stand it and came back saying Texas was barbarian—without any sign of health or aliveness. Eventually he left for San Francisco to look for work and we soon lost touch.

In Santa Fe, I joined a group called Women Who Write. It was fascinating. They were very strong, supportive, and knowledgeable. We met every Tuesday night and read something we'd written. Many of the women wrote poetry. Some of it was heavy, some light. I'd never enjoyed poetry before, but I really loved theirs. They wrote about lovers, husbands, family. One woman wrote fiction, and one other woman and myself wrote nonfiction. I wanted to write something about my experience with Jon. I also wanted to write a little booklet on home remedies.

The other women in the group were eating meat, dairy, eggs, chicken, and the usual things in the modern diet. They had tough exteriors, wore heavy boots, and carried knives in their belts and sometimes in their boots. They were very armored, yet they wrote the most sensitive poetry. I could see that their souls were gentle. One of the women came for dinner and asked me to go somewhere with her later. I couldn't go because I didn't feel comfortable leaving Jon. Later I learned she was lesbian.

That was one of my first encounters with homosexuality, and I was shocked. I realized many of the other women were also gay. It was clear to me then that their overly yang diet was the basic cause of their attraction to other women. They had become too yang and were repelled by men, who were also yang. Conversely, gay males were usually too yin. By eating too much salad, fruit, sweets, and dairy food, they lost their attraction to women, who are by nature yin. Macrobiotics was an amazing compass to begin to understand relationship and social problems like this.

Relations with My Ex

My ex-husband Joe and I continued to fight, even after our divorce. He didn't seem to understand or respect macrobiotics or what I was trying to do. He thought it was some strange cult and I was starving his son. I kept telling him that modern civilization and its way of eating centered on meat and sugar was the fad—at least compared to thousands of years of traditional society and eating whole grains and vegetables. But he couldn't hear anything I said, and I wasn't sympathetic to his views.

I had custody of Jon after our separation. When I went to California, Joe went nearly crazy. He scurried around for legal action and won some visitation rights. Jon was to see him three weeks during the summer.

When I went to Boston with Jon, Joe nearly had a coronary. "When are you going to settle down? You just got back from L.A. and now you want to take Jon way off up there." I wasn't very understanding myself. I said, "If you don't stop hassling me, I'll take him out of the country and you'll never see him."

That fall, Joe got remarried to Diana, a woman he met in his office. She was thirty-two and had two children, aged six and eight. She reminded me a lot of myself a few years back. She had bleached blond hair, dressed stylishly, and had many interests outside the home. I met her and liked her immediately. She and Joe moved into a big four-bedroom home in Irving, and Joe's mother came to live with them.

I visited Joe and Diana and talked to them about macrobiotics and the hope it held for Jon. They were very polite but unconvinced, as I was to find out later.

Jon visited them for a week at Christmas. I wrote ahead about Jon's diet and sent food with him on the plane, but it didn't help. He was extremely sick for several days when he returned.

Meanwhile, my financial situation had eroded. I had about

gone through all my money. I had lived fairly frugally in
Santa Fe. The only furniture we had was a sofa and a small
bedroom suite—a bed, chest of drawers, and mirror—for Jon.
I put a futon over his bed as he was accustomed to having a
bed and always liked that. And I slept on a futon. I made a
few clothes, but I never had my hair done, and the only
clothes I bought were two look-a-like jackets for the cold
weather and some warm shoes for us both. To top it off, I
discovered I had gum disease and had to have expensive
dental work. We were not poor, but we would be if I didn't
find a job.

I began applying for office work part-time but was told I
was overqualified. I applied for one receptionist job and they
had 107 applications. I applied for a counseling job that
required a master's degree plus three years' experience, and
they had forty applications. I didn't even get an interview.

To stay in Santa Fe with Jon, I asked for an increase in
child support. In our original settlement, I received no ali-
mony, just $150 a month for my son. They both worked,
and she received child support from her former husband.
They had several newer model cars, including a Lincoln,
and it seemed Joe could easily have afforded to contribute
more to Jon's upkeep. But he and Diana were unwilling to
support my lifestyle. Both their lawyer and mine felt I should
be out working rather than staying at home and cooking
and being there when Jon got home from school.

My first attorney was so intimidated by Joe's attorney that
he didn't even want to file a motion! Joe had hired one of the
most expensive law firms in Dallas to represent him. I talked
to another lawyer in Santa Fe. He really thought we could
win, but he said his fees could run as high as $2,000. And
he wanted to hire a clinical psychologist and put Jon through
an extensive series of tests. I just didn't feel right about it.
I wrote Joe and expressed hope that we could work it out
without the lawyers. But then Joe counterattacked. He filed
for increased visitation privileges—six weeks during the

summer, one week at Christmas, and one week at Easter. It was hard enough trying to heal Jon as it was. We needed one year of strict macrobiotic practice. Even three weeks was putting that in jeopardy. Another six weeks would put it out of reach. If Joe won those rights, our son might never get well.

My former husband's legal efforts put me through the emotional and financial wringer. In retaliation I called N.O.W. (the National Organization of Women) and got another lawyer. I felt she would be more sympathetic to my situation than a man. She charged $50 an hour, which I could ill afford. But I felt I had no alternative. Joe's lawyer kept requesting cancelled checks, records of deposits, tax returns, and check stubs for the past three years. I didn't keep much of that stuff. I felt they were trying to harrass me. The whole thing turned into a nightmare, and I was upset all the time.

As the winter wore on, Jon was inside more, and it was harder to take care of him. Despite his progress, he needed help with everything—bathing, dressing, straightening his room. He was difficult to manage, and I'd learned that I had to stay pretty laid back to be around him. Then too, he missed his father and talked about going back to live with him and eating their way. He lived for Saturday mornings when he could call him on the phone.

Although difficulties make us stronger, I began to feel a spiritual weariness from the constant struggle. One day a macrobiotic woman I knew asked me to take care of her children. One of them was only two and a half. He was so responsive to me and such a delight, it made me feel so much better having him around. And while the boy wasn't ecstatic over my cooking, he certainly seemed to take it for granted that he would be eating grains here. In contrast, Jon seemed to be very unappreciative.

At that time, I thought that there could be no compromise with the diet. Either Jon ate strictly for a year and got well or I might as well let him go back to his dad. I thought about taking Jon and leaving for a year so his father couldn't find him. But that was expensive and dangerous. In my distress, I asked Herman Aihara, the macrobiotic teacher in California, for his advice. I wrote him a letter on Easter:

Dear Herman,

I've been reading George Ohsawa's *Jack and Mitie* and learning a lot from it. He says in there, "If you understand the Order of the Universe, you can solve *any* problem." I must not understand it yet because I have one I haven't been able to solve, and I've thought about it for about a year now and studied a lot.

You may remember me—last year I wrote to you about my condition, and I have followed your recommendations pretty well. I took the whole year off to cook for myself and my son who is seven—and I've put a lot of time into our cooking, etc. My condition has improved in many ways, but in many others, it has not . . . it may even be worse. I think that it's not the food but the situation in my life that I have to resolve before my health will get any better.

My son is handicapped and has had a consultation with Michio who said it would take a year of strict macrobiotic eating (no oil, no salad, no fruit juices, etc.) to heal him. He is genetically normal but has many problems. But he's been to visit his Dad three times since then (a total of almost four weeks)—and he gets sick every time, plus he's not making the progress he should on the diet either. . . .

I've talked to him and his wife about Jon's diet (way of eating) and about the hope it holds for him. (As it stands now, he can't run, walk fast, hop well, etc. or speak well.) Not only are they unwilling to modify his diet at all while he visits but they are asking in court for longer visitation rights (6 weeks each summer).

I just can't accept this situation very philosophically. Is it ever "right" to take a child away from his father for a year or so?

I've been living on my savings from the sale of my home in Texas for over a year now, but I can't go on this way forever. I need to earn some money and yet Jon takes so much energy (he needs help bathing, dressing, etc.) and the cooking, too, takes time as you know.

You must be awfully busy, but I would appreciate your thoughts on this matter. Your judgment is higher than mine. I want to be fair to everyone, but I would give up almost anything to see my son run free. Thank you for your help.

Herman wrote back that I should be thankful that everyone loved Jon so much. He said Joe and Diana were "more macrobiotic" than I was. He said my judgment was lower than theirs because I didn't embrace them.

I was devasted. He didn't even think I was macrobiotic. I felt all my efforts had been for nothing.

Letting Go

There was a big back to my difficulties with Jon. I often said he's taught me everything I know because I'm always thinking, studying, and trying to figure out ways to establish peace and harmony.

And as much as I loved him it took a lot of energy to care for him. And then to have to always be fighting his dad about something was just too much. I decided to stop fighting. Herman hadn't made any specific recommendations, but it seemed clear that he felt Jon should be with his father. I wrote Joe that neither of us had had a moment's peace since our son was born. I asked him if they would keep Jon for the summer, and if it worked out he could stay with them and start school in Irving in the fall. I thought if they could see his problems, it might help. Difficulties make us strong. They make us seek true value.

Also I had to think about the order of things—healing *yourself* first, then healing your family and friends. My own condition was not what it should be because of the continual stress.

That spring, I had tried a symptomatic treatment which I

rarely do, taking olive oil and lemon juice, and passed many gallstones. Some were as large as a cherry, and many were medium size. To calm my nerves, I had four acupuncture treatments with Don, a student of Nakazone's. Later I saw the Sensei himself. He told me my pulses were fairly balanced, but I had no energy in my meridians. He recommended a direct moxa treatment. Moxa is a mugwort preparation, something like incense, that is burned directly on the skin to stimulate the energy flow. It was very powerful and strengthened my spleen, bladder, and kidney. It helped a lot and enabled me to do the spring cleaning and other chores I'd postponed.

In Santa Fe, I had studied the *I Ching*, the ancient Chinese Book of Changes. I learned to cast the fifty yarrow stalks for advice on my personal and spiritual development. Several months before, I had asked about letting Jon go back to his father's. The oracle counseled slow, steady progress (hexagram 53). The first changing line spoke of eating and drinking together and sharing one's good fortune with others. I took the image to be one of spreading macrobiotics. The second line portrayed a mother and father in conflict over their child. The commentary warned that if I went too far I would place myself and those close to me in danger. I felt I shouldn't be too inflexible in respect to Jon's diet or I might lose him altogether.

In June, I let Jon go back to live with his dad. I could hardly stay with him or without him. He couldn't slow down. He was always jabbering. Unless he had someone to play with, he never sat down. In the daytime I rationalized this decision but would wake up toward morning crying because I missed him. We had never been separated before.

I enjoyed my freedom for a while—reading, sewing, and cooking when I liked. During the summer, I continued to check out potential macrobiotic mates. I'd often find that while on paper and "according to the stars," we were eminently suitable, that when we met, we totally repelled each other. Still I persisted. I was visited by a man in Phoenix and later went to meet him and his children. I liked him in every way. He worked hard, cared about his children, was affectionate, and could even cook. Naturally, he wanted to be near his children. He asked me to move out and stay with him.

I thought about living in Arizona, but I felt very far away from my son. "It's as if there's an invisible cord attached to me (and Jon)," I noted, "and when he tugs a little bit on it, I come running no matter how far away I am." I decided to go back to Texas.

10.

Summers of '81 and '82

Oh, when the sun—
Refuse to shine—
Oh, when the sun refuse to shine—
Oh, Lawd, I want to be in that number,
When the sun refuse to shine.

FOR OVER FIFTEEN YEARS, Herman and Cornellia Aihara had led a macrobiotic summer camp in northern California. Located in the high Sierra Nevada mountains, the camp was held in a remote area called French Meadows. Two friends and I drove out from Texas in the summer of 1981.

A month earlier I had moved from Santa Fe to Denton. I wanted to be close to my son even if he was living with his father. I applied for a position as a school psychologist in the local school system and knew the woman who was in charge. But there were other applicants, and a man with a Ph.D. was selected. With my usual zest I had told them of my macrobiotic activities and later wondered whether or not my way of eating was a factor in the decision.

There was another opening for which I was qualified. It was in Lake Worth, on the west side of the Metroplex near Fort Worth, but I finally decided against it. I was afraid that I would not have time to cook for myself nor have the strength to resist eating luscious sugary treats with my colleagues.

There wouldn't be anything else coming up till fall, and Jon was with his dad visiting relatives in Missouri. I was free to travel. In late July, I drove out to French Meadows with

Gwen Luster, the woman with whom I had first taken macrobiotic cooking classes, and a friend of hers named Richard. We took my big '76 Caprice Classic Chevy and packed it to the gills, so the journey was very cramped. In addition to food, clothing, and sleeping bags, we had a tent and Richard's guitar.

When we left, I brought along a loaf of hard bread, pressure-cooked rice, rice balls, and stuff like that to eat along the way. They brought fruit, juice, and cookies and en route liked to stop and eat Mexican food and drink beer. I didn't know that traveling was very yangizing and that I should've adjusted my eating for the trip. Once on the road there was little choice—French fries, salads, breads made with refined flour. Gwen and I were too yang. We couldn't agree on the route and ended up taking the long way over the mountains. When Gwen was at the wheel, I'd see the speedometer inching over the 80 mph mark and was continually asking her to lower the speed. It was a scary 2,400-mile ride and a wonder we made it to French Meadows at all.

There were several hundred people camped out when we arrived. The majority were from the West Coast, but there were many individuals and families from other parts of the country. The food was too narrow, even for my taste. Cornellia Aihara's cooking was very yang and salty. Rice was pressure-cooked for nearly every meal. There were no salads, even boiled ones, and few desserts or snacks. No wonder everyone was binging. I was surprised to see tomato sauce and green peppers served to put over the rice and noodles! The nightshade vegetables are not normally served in macro-biotic households.

One day after lunch, I was asked if I'd like to go swimming and traipsed down to the river to find nearly everyone there swimming nude and one or two of the women stretched out naked on the rocks. It was a bit of a shock to me, but I tried not to gape and stare too much. I wanted to be part of the group and yet didn't feel comfortable going in the water naked in mixed company. I shed what I felt comfortable and went in for a brief swim but didn't return to this part of the river during the remaining days.

Although the leisure-time activities were more laid back than I was used to, I really enjoyed the teaching program. I met Ken Burns and took wild foods foraging and shiatsu classes. He was a long-time macrobiotic student and teacher from Boston who knew as much about wild plants as anyone and wrote many articles on the subject for *East West Journal*. He was very good to me and encouraged me to come to his class.

"Wild plants will give you a strong survival instinct," Ken told us.

I recalled that I had been raised on mostly wild food, especially rabbit, deer, and squirrel. I wondered if they had contributed to strengthening my will over the years.

At the bottom of the mountain, there was a store where everyone snuck out to binge on sweets, chips, and drinks. Ken didn't have a car, and I had one but was uneasy about driving down the mountain, so we would often go down the mountain together. I asked him a lot of questions about food and about life in general and was impressed with his endless patience. His recommendations nearly killed me, though. He said I should take dandelion root and dandelion leaves, with sautéed onions, to strengthen my kidneys. I asked him how often I should prepare them.

"Eat it for two or three times and then wait for the mixture to call you back to it," he told me.

When I got home, I was drinking pear juice by the quart to make balance for all the dandelions I was eating. The wild foods I prepared also sent me out to dances alone—something I had never done since giving up meat. I don't advise wild foods for women except in very small amounts—unless you like being wild and delirious, too.

I also enjoyed Jacques de Langre. He lectured on bread, salt, and fermented foods. He was another old-timer, a member of the first generation of American macrobiotic students who had studied with George Ohsawa or been deeply influenced by his teachings. He told us that most commercial sauerkraut and pickles are made with an "acidic acid" which destroys the lining of the stomach and large intestine, and it was important to make your own with an "alkaline acid." He made keeping a pickle crock sound like taking care of a baby. To nurse a good strain of lactobacillus, you had to constantly add new vegetables, grind and roast the rice bran just so, and every day without fail vigorously move every vegetable with two wooden spatulas scalded with hot water. I wondered if I was up to it!

Jacques had very strong opinions on all aspects of food and cooking. He said that taking in animal life or sugar created a barrier between you and nature and was the primary cause of fear. He felt that sugar overstimulates the nervous system so that you overreact to almost any situation. He believed you shouldn't use a refrigerator if you could help it and recommended you put the cooked rice into a woven basket with a damp towel over it instead. He said that every now and then eating differently gives us a very broad view. He believed that bread was as good quality a daily food as whole grains. He was the Johnny Appleseed of sourdough baking and preached that eating yeasted bread would give a twenty-year-old the blood quality of someone eighty. Early in my macrobiotic practice I had bought a $500 grain mill and made freshly milled flour for baking bread, muffins, and cookies. I consider that a major mistake in my early practice.

I had also used coarse grey sea salt. Jacques had recommended it in his lectures and writings. Harlan, my old California boyfriend (one of the super yang ones), used to buy it by the sackful and give it to his friends, as did another white-haired friend in Dallas. I later found that I preferred fluffy white sea salt in very moderate amounts and liked seasoning my dishes with tamari soy sauce, kombu, wakame, or miso instead of salt for variety.

Still, I admired Jacques's adventurous spirit. He also gave

exercises every morning in the cold river, but I didn't go to them. I about froze to death at night. The day before we left, I discovered some extra quilts and put one over my own thin polyester sleeping bag to keep warm. Though greatly improved, my condition was still a little weak. I brought a backstand with me to lean against during classes.

The one thing that stayed with me from Jacques's talks was not a technique or method. It was something he said about family. George Ohsawa and Michio Kushi had also said it many times, but I liked the way he put it: "Hold the ancestral influences dear to your hearts. They are your best guide. See what they were eating. Try to search back and find what they ate."

Another stimulating speaker was Jim Moon. He talked on calcification and the harmful effects of taking artificial Vitamin D. He said that it increases the absorption of calcium (more than we need) and could lead to kidney stones, arthritis, or other diseases caused by calcification in the soft tissues and arteries. He told how he challenged the dairy council, and it cost him his doctorate. He advised me to eat grapefruit juice for my condition. But Ken Burns said no, it was too extreme. The teachers seldom agreed on anything. Jacques de Langre would be teaching, and Cornellia would listen in the back and shake her head. The only thing there was unanimity on was nut butter. It was better to eat it with salt and thereby balance its heavy oil and fat content. Jacques's wife, Yvette, said you should make babies sleep all through the night and not nurse them. "If you feed them on demand, you teach them to constantly want to be satisfied and exhaust the mother," she said. Other mothers with equally long macrobiotic experience disagreed and said she was too yang.

I also met Sandy Rothman, editor of the *G.O.M.F. Newsletter*. We had corresponded for about a year. Only a month earlier I had written:

Have you found, as I have, that there are almost as many interpretations of macrobiotics as there are people? It always amazes me to see what people describe as balanced eating. But the biggest problem as I see it and as I've gathered from reading is the idea that they can smoke dope, eat honey, or whatever and not have to pay the price for it—if you know what I mean—the mind-set that that's not harmful to their health.

Once we met at the camp, Sandy and I didn't spend much time together, though he liked to play the banjo, and I joined a small group of campers who sang, danced, and drank beer around the campfire in the evenings. Later, I saw him on several occasions and came to count him as a good friend. I also met Carl Ferre, who sold books for G.O.M.F. and Julia who later became his wife.

Aside from meeting eligible men, my main interest in attending summer camp was to develop my cooking. I had learned a lot in Boston, but had a long way to go. I didn't know how to make tempeh, and the only pickles I knew how to make were short-term brine pickles.

All food in the camp was cooked over open wood fires. Tea was kept simmering for anyone who was thirsty. People drank a lot of mugwort tea. Ken Burns picked the mugwort in the wilds. I helped with the cooking. There were different shifts. Like most women, I am active in the mornings and give out early in the evening. I volunteered for the early shift and was up, dressed, and out fetching water or cutting vegetables by 6 or 6:30. I really enjoyed working in the kitchen but questioned some things. They nearly washed the rice to death. Cornellia said it put a lot of *ki* into old grain. Also, the miso soup was too strong for me. It was served twice a day. There was a low-salt variety for children. I tried to eat that instead.

Getting too yang is probably the most common problem among macrobiotic people. Yinning out is less frequent, and when it happens it's usually because people are taking too much salt, miso, or tamari soy sauce and being attracted to sweets, fruits, and drinks.

One of the special guests at the camp was a Japanese

woman whose name I forget but who had been a secretary to George Ohsawa. She gave cooking demonstrations and had a rich gourmet style. One day she prepared a pretty dish combining two kinds of squash served with a thick, Bechamel-like sauce with flour and oil. She also made nori rolls filled with soba noodles instead of rice. That was the first time I'd had that delicacy. She was also in charge of the gomasio for the camp. A pity, for when it came to salt and seasoning, she was not so creative. From her appearance, I could tell that she was way too contracted from overuse of salt. Her head and shoulders were bent, her face had no expression, her features were drawn, and her hands habitually hung down limply at her side. Once I saw her eating a teaspoon of raw salt out of her hand. I said to myself, "God help me not to become like that."

Such rigidity, as a result of taking too much salt, is a big problem in macrobiotics. One of the most welcome changes the Kushis made in their dietary recommendations was to cut the use of salt, miso, and tamari soy sauce in recipes by about three-quarters. They explained that America is more yang than Japan, which is very humid, and therefore people here require much less salt, miso, tamari, and other seasonings. After they cut back salt, they found their students were much more comfortable, less dogmatic in their thinking, and able to stay in one place. In my experience, it is certainly true.

The camp marked my introduction to chanting. The problem was I couldn't understand what was being said. It was all in Japanese, Sanskrit, or some foreign language. I gathered it had something to do with greeting the sun and bowing to the earth and praying for ancestors and dead relatives. I felt uncomfortable about the religious part, especially when I couldn't understand it. I felt it was all right for the Japanese, but didn't see its application to me. I didn't keep it up when I got home. It was much later before I began to appreciate chanting and incorporate it into my daily practice.

A main reason for coming to Summer Camp was to get

more insight into helping my son. Although I was shocked at Herman's reply to my letter a few months earlier, I respected his judgment. In person, Herman Aihara was very quiet. He didn't talk much, but I could feel his gentle strength. In his lecture, he encouraged everyone to start vegetable gardens as soon as possible and recommended singing as the best breathing exercise of all. He also talked about using alcohol to dissolve excess fat and protein, and I picked up the idea of using beer as a yin balancing factor to discharge some of the old meat, poultry, and eggs I had taken.

Compared to her husband, Cornellia was a dynamo. She worked herself out managing the kitchen and was always talking, laughing, prodding, or otherwise in motion.

One day I summoned up the courage to sit with the Aiharas at dinner. I wanted to ask them about Jon. I'd been considering letting him go back and live with his father.

"Right now, family's more important than food," Cornellia told me.

I was disappointed that she didn't have any confidence in me or my dream of healing my son, but I respected her opinion and considered her advice in my final decision. At that time I didn't see how just the two of us could make it. And after all, the bigger the front, the bigger the back. Something positive could come from my son returning to his father.

After ten days, camp was over. When we came down the mountain, Gwen, Richard, and I hit the first big supermarket. I bought a package of carob cookies and ate almost half of it by myself. In addition, we stocked up on beer and fruit juice and then went hunting for a good restaurant with a salad bar. We satiated ourselves at a Chinese restaurant and were finally ready for the trip back. We drove back through Colorado and went through Aspen. There was still snow on the tips of the mountains that could be seen from a distance, and the air was crisp and clear even in late summer. It was the most beautiful place I'd ever seen. John

Denver became macrobiotic about the same time I did. I learned later his home was in Aspen. To me that showed what strong intuition he was born with or acquired. Someday I would like to visit him there.

In Denver, Richard left us to go mountain climbing. Gwen and I hopscotched our way back to Texas via health food stores along the way. We munched honey-sweetened carrot cake and had raw fruit and fruit juices and other snacks to balance the salty food we had eaten at camp, the summer heat, and the long drive home.

Return to Texas

Back in Texas, I moved to a house on Lake June Road in Balch Springs. It was owned by Norman Ralston, the macrobiotic veterinarian. He and Helen were living in a town house in Garland and had several investment properties. The house in Balch Springs was near his clinic in East Dallas, and he liked to come there for lunch and take a nap in the afternoons. I was hired to do the cooking, and both Norman and Helen came every day for lunch and supper. I also bought the groceries, cleaned house, and gave shiatsu massages for which I received $300 a month plus room and board.

Norman and Helen were fun to be around. They were warm, affectionate, and we laughed and talked a lot, and sometimes we all went dancing together at a big ballroom called the Four Seasons. They were like family to me. As a veterinarian, Norman was also always taking in stray or homeless pets. One time, he adopted a goat and named it Buffy. He brought it back to the house and let it graze in the fenced-in yard. But Buffy was not content with the grass on the lawn and started to butt up against the wall and try to get in the house.

"Y'all got to come and get this goat," I phoned him frantically one day at work. "Buffy's trying to take over this place."

They came and corralled it. We tried to figure out the
cause of the goat's extreme yang behavior. Norman had been
feeding it a special natural animal mixture of his own, and
I had been giving it leftover rice, miso soup, and vegetables.
Maybe it just wanted more good home cooking.

Something like this was always happening. There was
always a crisis. Another time, I got locked out. I used to
bring Jon over on Saturday mornings. He was living with
his father and step-mother in Irving, about twenty-five miles
away. One morning we arrived to find that the gate to the
house in Balch Springs was locked. I started bawling and felt
like I'd been shut out. Norman and Helen always left the
gate locked, though not the back door, and thought I had a
key. I phoned and they came right over and unlocked it. But it
was a traumatic experience.

A lot of people asked Norman for his advice on their
health problems. As a veterinarian, he always told them that
he treated animals, not people. Sometimes he would refer
them to Terrance or some other macrobiotic friend in Dallas.
Sometimes he would refer them to me.

I met a woman who lived near Houston. Her husband had
liver cancer and was too sick to travel. I went over with her
the foods in the Standard Macrobiotic Diet and helped her
shop.

"He's not going to die of cancer," she told me. Then she
phoned one day in alarm after beginning the new way of
eating. "He's belching a lot," she said.

I asked her why, but she didn't know. I went through the
foods he was taking and found that she had bought green tea
and was giving it to him as a regular beverage. I encouraged
her to stop it and give him bancha twig tea instead.

The next time I talked with her, a few days later, I learned
he had passed away.

I don't know whether the tea had anything to do with it.
At the Kushi Institute we had been taught that green tea is
not suitable as a daily beverage. In fact, from my under-

standing of yin and yang, I believe it can stress the liver and
cause it to discharge toxins too rapidly.

However, in this case, as in most others, it was not a
question of one or two items. It was a question of the whole
past way of eating and immediate need for proper cooking.
Although the woman may have a lot of experience and be
a good cook by ordinary standards, macrobiotic cooking has
to be learned from scratch.

Since then I have counseled many people and found over
and over again that new people simply don't realize the
importance of studying cooking.

Friends call now and ask me how many classes they need to
learn to cook. I don't know how to answer that because the
study of cooking is a lifetime experience. We can always
learn from more experienced cooks, although the most important factor in proper cooking is our own condition. Generally,
someone who has cooked macrobiotically for five years makes
food with a very different quality and energy than someone
who is just starting. Someone with ten or twenty years'
experience is superior, in most cases, to someone with five.
But we can all learn from each other.

I liked cooking in Balch Springs, and the environment was
pleasant, but it became too much for me. Norman and Helen
started inviting other people over for meals. Flora Lee, the
office manager at the clinic, came regularly. Sometimes the
whole staff would come over to eat. I was flattered that
Norman wanted to show off my cooking to everyone and get
them started on macrobiotics, but cooking for ten to twelve
people was more than I had bargained for.

To get out of the house and relax, I took a part-time job
housesitting for a woman's cat. She worked for American
Express and had a lovely apartment, clothes, and a swimming
pool. She was very gracious and invited me to stay with her.
But the house had an electric stove and synthetic carpeting,
and I declined.

Adventures with Lino

I tried to work out different schedules with Norman, but I was too exhausted to continue. Finally I met a woman named Coco, who was vegetarian, and moved in with her. She lived in Farmers Branch, a suburb to the north of Dallas, It was the first time I had lived with another woman since the early '60's. Coco was a thoughtful, nurturing young woman and we got along well. I taught cooking classes at home and enjoyed it.

In Denton, some people at a pot luck told me about Lino Stanchich, a senior macrobiotic teacher and counselor and encouraged me to write him and try to get him to come to Dallas to teach. He was in New York at the time. I wrote him in December, and we started corresponding. He said he would do a consultation for me, and I sent back a two- to three-page case history. I was ecstatic. I sought not only his advice but also his companionship. On one occasion, he wrote that he would be coming through Texas and would like to visit. I thought he was coming especially to see me. I didn't know he had a girlfriend. Finally he saw how happy I was about his visit and told me he'd had two people with him, his daughter and another woman.

I had just started studying astrology and directionology. "Be cautious," I wrote in big letters on my calendar. Ironically, I thought I was being most cautious. It would be years before I could see the mistakes I was about to make.

Lino arrived with his daughter and friend, Jane. He was every bit as striking as I had imagined. He was tall, robust, and had a deep voice that seemed to come from the *hara*, the energy center in the lower intestines. But the most yang feature was his shaven head. He looked like a macrobiotic Yul Brynner. Originally from Yugoslavia, he had a slight accent that contributed to the glamour and mystery surrounding him. Aveline Kushi has said that Lino has the strongest constitution of any macrobiotic teacher she has ever met. I agree.

Lino and I spent a lot of time with each other over the next two or three days. We went off on errands, while Jane stayed home and did the cooking. It wasn't clear to me what their relationship was. He was in his late forties or early fifties, and she appeared fifteen years younger.

Lino talked a lot about food. He made a fist and told me not to eat more than a handful of rice. He said I should prepare bulgur for breakfast, mix bulgur and rice together for lunch, and then have rice for dinner. He implied that I walked like a man but would be all right in a year or two. This was true in a way. I wore jeans all the time and had a big belt buckle. He told me wearing skirts was good for the ovaries and would make me more feminine. He recommended two *donko* (premium Shiitake mushrooms) per day as well as dried persimmon to discharge old meat and fish. I wanted to improve my health and love life and followed his suggestions religiously.

One of the things Lino brought with him was liquid sea minerals. Mr. Muramoto, a student of George Ohsawa's, a noted herbalist, and author of *Healing Ourselves*, had developed them on the West Coast. They were made from boiling liquid sea salt or concentrate and packaged in small brown bottles that sold for $3 or $4 each. Lino agreed with Muramoto that most macrobiotic people were not getting enough minerals. We all took them, a half teaspoon a day. I noticed the effects right away. My period came suddenly. I had the last one only two weeks before. Then I experienced severe menstrual cramps. I hadn't had many menstrual cramps in the past few years. I also had intense crying spells. One night we visited the same friends who'd encouraged me to contact Lino, and I had to excuse myself and went outside and bawled in an open field for an hour. Back home, Lino did a ginger compress on my ovaries and gave me some tea with yinnie syrup. After he went to bed, I got up and ate more yinnie syrup straight from the jar.

Despite these severe reactions, I didn't connect my problems with the sea minerals. I knew they were yangizing, but thought my crying and other symptoms were a necessary discharge of excess yin.

Over the next four to six weeks, I flipped out. I got super yang. I cleaned out my closet and gave away my beautiful wardrobe that I'd accumulated over the years. I got rid of everything except for my sheepskin jacket and one or two coats. I dispensed with my Levis, my tailor-made skirts and blouses, shoes, bags, and other expensive things. I bought white clothes, especially long flowing skirts and very feminine white blouses. I sold my $1,200 sofa for a small fraction of its value. I felt the material was not natural enough and may have been treated with chemicals. I never considered covering it with a cotton spread.

After work, I'd ride a bike all around the neighborhood. It was the first time in years I'd ridden. Then I'd fix dinner and after dinner want to sing. I'd go to the park and sing my heart out. My favorite was the Southern gospel, "Just a Closer Walk with Thee," and John Denver's "Boy From the Country." I felt I was on the same wavelength as Jesus and some of the rock stars and it was my mission to save the world. I wrote Michio in Boston and told him about my dream. I also told him that the articles in *East West Journal* were too complicated for the ordinary person to understand and they needed to be simplified. I wrote Alex Jack, *EWJ's* editor, and offered him my journalistic services. He wrote back, politely inviting me to submit an article, but I never did.

Mentally, I was very sharp. I loved my work at the Dallas County Public Schools typing out psychological reports. I could type for six or seven hours without a break and churn out three or four reports a day. My co-workers were amazed at my industriousness. I took my tape recorder and sang hymns at lunch. They may have thought I was a little odd though, as I shunned traditional office attire of suits and tailored dresses for white flowing skirts, soft cotton blouses, and scarf headbands.

There was an area set aside in the office for people to eat lunch and a Coke machine for soft drinks. Most people brought fried chicken, hamburgers, and bologna and cheese sandwiches. I usually ate my lunch alone in the park across the street.

Being different from the crowd was made easier because I had a dream—a vision not only of becoming healthier myself but also of becoming a great spiritual teacher who would talk to throngs of people in my white flowing gown. I found a purple tassel to tie around my waist, an icthys (Christian fish symbol) to wear around my neck, and some barefoot sandles like Jesus was shown wearing in Bible illustrations. Mornings, I'd wake up at 4 or 5 A.M. and visualize receiving messages from a higher being.

In a letter to Lino, I tried to convey what I heard God instructing me:

> Barbara Gale (I hate it when He calls me Barbara Gale!), you've learned that the wisdom of the world is foolishness with me; you've not been deceived. You've known loss in my behalf; now you will know gain. You've known ridicule and hate; now you will know admiration and love. You've given up (temporarily) your son by birth, now you will mother all who seek to know the Truth.

At work I came across an article in *National Geographic* about salmon returning upsteam. I identified with the symbolism and felt I was returning to my ancestral source and going to have a spiritual child.

The only problem with this was that I could not conceive. Eight years earlier, I had had my tubes tied as a form of birth control. The subject originally came up about a year before Jon was born. My husband and I had been trying unsuccessfully to have a child ever since we were married. One wintry evening I snuggled up to my husband in our king-size bed. I hated the big bed because the distance from

one side to the other echoed the distance in our relationship.
I always liked to be close to him at night. I told Joe that if
I didn't get pregnant by my next birthday. I wanted to have
a tubal ligation because I didn't want to wake up one day
when I was an old woman and find myself pregnant. I'd heard
too much about change-of-life babies.

After our son was born, I still experienced problems
connected with his birth. I didn't feel responsive to my
husband, and our marriage was not going well. I had tried
various forms of birth control, but they all had disadvantages.
Tubal ligation sounded ideal.

I went to the hospital in Irving and had a one-day operation. I was still nursing Jon and told the doctors that I
didn't want much anesthesia so I would be able to be with
him that night. I made myself come out from under the drugs
and literally ordered Joe to come to the hospital and check
me out so I could go home the same day of the surgery and
not stay another night away from Jon. When I got home,
I took Jon in my arms, and he started nursing. We were so
happy to be back together. We had never been apart that long
before.

I thought the operation was very efficient. All they do is
go in and tie the fallopian tubes so you can't conceive. I was
groggy from the anesthetic for a couple of days, but other
than that I was not aware of any physiological changes. I
didn't know anything about *ki* or energy blockages. Since
becoming macrobiotic, I started to learn about meridians,
energy flow, and the body's vibrational constitution. Lino told
me that operations, such as tubal ligation in women and
vasectomy in men, disrupted the smooth flow of natural
electromagnetic energy in the body. My operation even may
have contributed to my ovarian tumors. As in the case of
which came first, the chicken or the egg, I didn't know
whether I was attracted to the operation because I was so
yang to begin with or whether I became overly yang as a
result. It was before my dietary changes. In any event, I must

have been very yang not to want more children, and after the operation I became even more materialistic.

When Lino came, I still had some pain or discomfort in my right ovary. Jon was staying with his father. I felt empty with him gone. I wanted to correct whatever was wrong with me that left me alone and without a family. I also read an article in the *East West Journal* about how tubal ligation and vasectomy diminish your sexual polarity and attraction to the other sex. Lino told me he thought my sterilization could be reversed.

At the teachers' lounge at work, I found some material on laparoscopy. It was a surgical procedure to examine and X-ray the pelvic region. I went to see the surgeon. He said he would do the laparoscopy and see whether it was possible to reverse the tubal ligation. Sometimes it was possible, other times it wasn't, depending on how the fallopian tubes had been severed. Lino recommended that I have the operation done under local rather than general anesthetic. He didn't want me to have any more drugs than necessary.

I arranged to have the initial operation in Brookhaven Medical Center in Farmers Branch. Lino had gone to California, and we talked occasionally on the phone. I thought he was coming back and hoped we would live together. He wrote that we were very close physically, spiritually, and emotionally. That, coupled with my past experience, was enough for me to discount his relationship with Jane. I didn't think I'd go into surgery alone.

The operation and its sequel cost over $7,000. Fortunately, I had health insurance at my new job, which covered most of it. I went in early in the morning. It was the first week in July and very hot. The doctors gave me a local anesthetic in the abdominal area and then put carbon dioxide in my body to blow up the abdomen, making it possible to put an instrument through the navel and inspect the abdominal cavity and ovarian tubes. They also injected a radio-opaque dye through the vagina and cervix so these organs would show

up on the X-rays. My bed was on a slant, and as I lay back
I intuitively started chanting. I recited a chant that Michio
had recently taught in a seminar. I was so afraid—more
afraid than I had ever been before and maybe since. The
carbon dioxide made it difficult to breathe. I moaned and
groaned and gasped for breath. The doctor couldn't see my
face because of a screen that had been put up to keep me
from seeing what he was doing. There was little pain in the
abdominal area, but the pain in my chest was excruciating. I
couldn't speak. I felt I was a goner. Then a nurse grabbed my
hand. It was like a bolt of energy. The doctor eased up on
the CO_2, saying perhaps I'd had enough, and I felt the life
force returning.

Afterwards, Dr. Howard, my chief doctor, showed me the
x-rays and the blockage and said he'd have to study them
further but felt sure he could repair one side and perhaps
both. I was wheeled back to a room to rest a few hours before
going home.

My spirit was undiminished, and I remarked to Dr.
Howard, "I'm going to make you famous."

He chuckled, "Oh, you are, are you?"

I'm sure I looked like the last person in the world who
could make anybody famous.

I thought eventually I would have a great spiritual child
and wanted to give him credit. At home, I had a large print
of one of Leonardo da Vinci's drawings of the Madonna and
Child. Like Mary, the mother of Jesus, I was macrobiotic and
felt I would be giving my son every advantage. By eating
carefully during my pregnancy, I would ensure that he had a
wonderful constitution for his mission to bring peace to the
world. I always considered the child would be a boy, never
a girl.

I had been entertaining thoughts like this since taking the
sea minerals, though sometimes my mind began to waiver.
I thought maybe the child had already been born. Maybe it
was Jon. I didn't know any more what was real. All I knew
was that I was incredibly intuitive. When I put my mind on

something, I could manifest it. Soon after putting up the big picture of Mary and Jesus, I attracted a small picture just like it in a magazine in a bookstore. It seemed like an omen.

When I returned to the hospital for my results, Dr. Howard was sitting behind his massive desk covered with folders and other paraphernalia. He asked if I really wanted to have another child if I could. I got the impression he didn't think I was too old. He went on to tell me that the medical diagnosis was encouraging. The doctors found that the fallopian tube had been snipped close to the uterus. Scar tissue had developed, but it could be removed and the passageway reconstructed.

The second operation, called a reanastomosis, was scheduled for two weeks later. This particular procedure required a needle smaller than a sewing needle and was so intense the doctor scheduled only one a week. He had three other surgeons assist him. Just before the anesthesia, someone asked him if he'd like some coffee.

"I never drink anything before surgery," he said.

"Thank God," I thought.

Lino had gone to northern California to attend the Aihara's Summer Camp. I felt sure he'd come for the big surgery. He called and expressed his concern. He must have thought I was a little crazy. He and Jane often commented what a "spiritual" person I was. Maybe he didn't realize that the sea minerals were making me lose touch with reality. He had told me some time back to stop them. I cut down, but by then the damage had been done.

I had the second operation under general anesthesia. For some reason I'd expected it to be similar to other procedures I'd had in the past. I had recovered from the tonsillectomy within a week and the bladder surgery in two or three weeks. Of course, I was younger then too but not macrobiotic. So I had no particular fears the night before the surgery. I'd told my brother and sister it was considered major surgery, but that it wasn't anything to worry about.

The operation took some four and a half hours. When I

woke up, my whole body wracked with pain. I was lying on a cushiony foam mattress but couldn't raise myself up. The surgeons had made a small incision and moved my intestines around in order to get to the fallopian tubes. I later learned they did this for cosmetic purposes, so the woman wouldn't have a big scar. It was a perfect example of what in macrobiotics we call "back and front"—more problems healing now in exchange for a scar-free tummy later on.

When I came to, the hospital staff offered me pain pills, but I was already too druggy from the anesthetic and refused them. Lino hadn't returned, but I didn't go to the hospital alone. My macrobiotic friends rallied to my side. Tom Tatum, a young friend, sat through the operation and came to see me daily while I was in the hospital. He'd sit on the bed and hold my hand. The doctors and nurses thought we were engaged and I was having my tubes untied so we could have a family.

My friends brought me strong miso soup, brown rice, and other macrobiotic foods, but I couldn't eat anything yang. All I wanted was juice and light things. I had brought some wine with me to the hospital and used that whenever I wanted to ease the pain. One immediate result of the operation was I started smoking again. I hadn't smoked in nine or ten years. But suddenly I had a craving to smoke. Probably it was an intuitive response to try to yangize myself after the surgery.

I was in the hospital for a week. Dr. Howard marveled at my recovery. He told me I had had a severe reaction to the anesthetic and was the same as "dead on the operating table." It was a wonder I was alive. The operation had been a success, but I had almost died.

In retrospect, it was clear that modern medicine should be relied on only to save a person's life or repair a broken bone. But if for some reason a person chooses to have a surgical procedure, it shouldn't be done in July, the most yang time of the year. Rather it should be done in the winter and

ideally in a cooler climate so that the natural, slightly more
yang way of eating will accelerate the healing.

Flight to California

After the second operation, I started to take sea minerals
again to balance the drugs. I wanted to see Lino and felt if I
could see him he would help me recover. After resting a few
days at home, I took Jon and flew to San Francisco. I was so
so weak during the layover in Utah that I lay on the floor in
the airport. I couldn't sit up straight in a chair. Jon had to
take care of himself for hours while we waited for our plane.

In California, a man named Grady Bollinger met us at the
airport and drove us to the George Ohsawa Macrobiotic
Foundation. We just missed Lino. After summer camp, he had
headed on back to Southern California.

In Oroville, I saw Herman Aihara briefly. I had written
the lead article in the February issue of *The G.O.M.F.
Newsletter* on adventures in healing my son. Herman remembered us and said I could stay at the Center. He said he would
see me in a day or two, but he never did. After the first night
in a motel, Jon and I moved into the G.O.M.F. house. I was
so weak I could hardly climb the stairs to the bedroom on the
second floor.

Cornellia Aihara phoned once. I was so weak, I told her,
"I think I'm going to die." She didn't comment. Instead, she
said "Let me speak to Gwen." My friend Gwen Luster from
Texas was in the process of divorcing her husband, and
Cornellia was naturally concerned.

I couldn't understand why Cornellia didn't respond to my
plea. I knew she was very yang from summer camp. Like
everyone else, I guessed she was exhausted from French
Meadows and off recuperating somewhere.

Later I realized she probably hadn't heard me. My voice
was so weak, it may not have registered, and like most
Japanese she had a hard time understanding spoken English.

Or she may have felt (like I do) that everyone is responsible for their own health and well-being and wondered why I was there.

Some men came from summer camp to repair the roof, and a few women stopped by from summer camp on their way home and cooked one or two meals, but no one was in charge of the daily cooking.

For the next several days, Jon and I survived as best we could. By now my skin and the whites of my eyes had turned yellow, and I'd lost weight even though the abdomen itself was swollen. I still wore white day and night, often wearing the same soft white embroidered gown I slept in as a dress. I had no energy to wash or bathe. I could hardly lift a glass of water to my mouth. One of the men who kept coming through the room we were in to get to the roof stopped long enough to instruct me to make my bed. My friend Sandy Rothman, editor of the newsletter, took us by the store to get some groceries and brought some food he had cooked. But he was busy and didn't stay. Finally, Jon was so hungry I managed to go downstairs with him and walk half a block to an ordinary restaurant to get something to eat.

We bought fresh melons that soon disappeared and were not replaced. I got scared and thought I must be dying, so decided to try to go home but couldn't find anyone to take me to the airport. Everybody was busy.

With help from Jon, who brought me water and helped me downstairs, I phoned Larry Brown, a friend in Texas. Larry had been macrobiotic longer than anybody I had met besides the Japanese. In fact, he had been living in Chico, California, in 1963 when several dozen macrobiotic people left New York in a caravan for the West Coast. It was the time of the Berlin Crisis, and they hoped to find a safe haven in case of nuclear war. Larry had welcomed the first families to come to Chico, including the Aiharas. He soon become macrobiotic and studied with George Ohsawa, who came to Chico and taught during the next several summers.

Larry had been in the right place at the right time, and I respected his judgment and intuition. Besides, he had originally encouraged me to go to the West Coast.

"Your fortune lies in California," he told me.

I felt that some day I would have millions of dollars. During my trip to California, I wanted to investigate real estate holdings so I could have a say in the quality of rice grown and in the future direction of Chico-San, the macrobiotic food company. Such were my delusions. The truth of the matter was that I came home wagging my tail behind me.

I told Larry I was in a bad way and needed help. He arranged for a friend to pick us up and take us to the airport in San Francisco. Larry met us in Dallas and literally saved my life.

Turning Point

Earlier that spring, I had moved to Oak Cliff, a beautiful older section of Dallas. Lino told me that I needed a better environment in which to heal myself. Oak Cliff had rolling hills, large trees, and houses that were two and three stories high. It was very much like some New England or Midwestern neighborhood set in the middle of flat, barren Dallas and its one-story bedroom communities. My apartment had hardwood floors—virtually impossible to find in most of the city and suburbs—and I asked the landlord not to install a carpet. They actually had a gas stove so I didn't have to have one put in as I had done in the past. About 90 percent of the stoves in Dallas are electric. I don't understand people thinking they can practice macrobiotics while cooking on an electric range.

After coming back from California, I was still very weak and had no energy to clean. Boxes were still piled up from the recent move and the apartment was a mess. Tom Tatum came over and did the dishes, but many of my friends stayed away. My skin, including the whites of my eyes, had turned yellow. My neighbor upstairs—the one I'd earlier given Jon's bedroom suit, some silverware, and a camera to and who was an active "Christian" bringing me healing cassette tapes— charged in one day with a girlfriend demanding that I go to the doctor for treatment for hepatitis. She further told me that they'd contacted the health department and were prepared to have me evicted if I didn't agree to medical treatment. I refused. Maybe she found out it would be too expensive to go that route as she decided to have an injection herself instead. Another couple came to see me and when I didn't answer the front door went around to the bedroom in back and were shocked at my appearance. They, too, decided to stay away.

Tom would bring food and grocieries but leave them at the door and not come in and visit. Leslie Tolleson often shopped for me when she shopped for herself, even when I was unable to pay her. And yang and caring Larry scoffed at the idea that I was infectious. He'd lovingly rub my feet and sit and talk to me and sometimes give me polarity therapy. He always came when I needed him, but I definitely tried not to take advantage and to do as much for myself as I could.

One of the things I tried to do as soon as possible was the laundry. I always liked to have clean, fresh clothes and towels and bed linens. The nearest laundromat was two miles away, so I'd pile the clothes into the car, often making two to three trips for one small load. At the laundry, Sarah Fatheree, the attendant who mothered a number of women in the community, would come out to the car and carry the clothes into the laundry for me and load them up again when I left.

I was not the only one in trouble that summer. A gay man named Sebastian St. James had lost his apartment, couldn't find work, and was eating out of trash cans. His clothes were stored in some "friends' " garage, but he owed them money, and they wouldn't return them until he paid his debts. Sebastian started out by sleeping in my car, and I gave him leftovers to eat. He'd just heard of macrobiotics and was so

hungry that he was always grateful for whatever I prepared
for him. Eventually I let him stay in the house. Sebastian was
even more disorderly than I was, but it strengthened me to
have someone to take care of and talk to. I let him know
right away that he was not eating with just any ordinary
person but a woman who'd been chosen to have a great
spiritual child whose influence would be as widespread as
Jesus's. I think he just about believed it, too.

My way of eating was very erratic after I got out of the
hospital. My liver was so sore that it hurt when I walked, and
I had to move very slowly to minimize the pain. I couldn't
eat pressure-cooked rice at all and had little energy to cook
anything. I started eating bean burritos at Taco Bell down
the street and was soon gulping down cheese sauce, hot
sauce, and eating jalapeno peppers. I craved yin, and to
balance the excess minerals, I started drinking coffee and
occasionally Cokes. Looking back, I think the hot sauce
helped open up the lungs which were contracted from the sea
minerals.

This was one of the few times I'd really binged since being
macrobiotic. My abdomen was very large, and I looked
pregnant. I felt I must have conceived like Mary and
ordered maternity clothing from Sears. When you're pregnant,
you're expected to binge, so I thought it was all right. I
didn't realize that my intestines had remained swollen after
the operation.

I didn't know what the cause of my problem was or what to
do. I didn't eat any fish or seafood at the time. According to
macrobiotic theory, woman could never be happy eating
animal food. Naturally I wanted to be happy, so I strictly
avoided all animal food, including fish. Now I know it
would have been very strengthening for me at the time. I
got some relief from acupuncture. The Ralstons had introduced me to Mr. Nabeshima, a Japanese acupuncturist in
North Dallas. I went to see him as often as I could, and his
treatment would lessen the pain and increase my vitality.

And feeling that he and his wife cared for me made a big difference.

At home, I practiced visualization. During the middle of the day, from about 11 A.M. to 3 P.M., I couldn't get out of bed. I would lie for hours and imagine healing light entering my back. I focused on the heart-lung chakra, though I didn't know it at the time. And I listened to music and saw myself dancing around the room.

The visualization helped a little, but my weight kept falling. I dropped to 89 pounds. I lost my "curves" and with that my will to live faltered. But I hated to die with everything such a mess. Boxes from the move in late June lay about unpacked. And I thought of Jon. He was just nine years old. Who would tell him about macrobiotics?

For the last few years, I'd been surviving by teaching at home and selling silver left over from my real estate ventures. One day I went to my closet and found there wasn't any silver left. I was stunned. I thought I had another box salted away. Maybe it had been stolen, or more likely I had already sold it. In any event, I had no retirement, no savings, and no bank account. I applied for food stamps. I was told I had to show I could pay for my rent. My brother signed a form pledging to give me $100 a month, but by some fluke that was just enough to disqualify me for the stamps. When I hit rock bottom, I had taken almost no solid food for forty days. I consoled myself thinking that, like Jesus, I was fasting in the wilderness.

What little money I could scrounge, I spent on burritos and chips. I was so ashamed of binging that I snuck Cokes into my own bedroom because I didn't want Sebastian, whom I had lectured to about the evils of sugar, to see them. One night in early September, after sipping Coke in the privacy of my bedroom and chanting for 10 minutes, I walked into the kitchen with a new awareness. I recalled some of my study of yin and yang. I knew Cokes could discharge excess minerals and animal protein, but that was the extreme way.

For the first time I connected the sea minerals with my problems. I realized that my whole life was out of balance.

I went outside and dumped the rest of the liquid sea concentrate under a big tree. I apologized to the tree and hoped it wouldn't pull itself up by the roots like I had and go dancing deliriously around the neighborhood. That was the beginning of my return to sanity.

11.

My Planetary Family

I heard the voice of my Savior
Telling me still to fight on;
He promised never to leave me,
Never to leave me alone.

THE SURGERY WAS ANOTHER WATERSHED IN MY LIFE. It took only four and an half hours on the operating table, but over four and a half years to recover from. I was weak in every way, physically, emotionally, and spiritually.

Later that summer, Michio Kushi and two senior macrobiotic teachers, Bill Spear and Dr. Keith Block, came to Houston for a workshop. It was affordable, only about $65. I took the last money I had and went to Houston. I stayed with a woman whom I had previously cooked for. She had some kind of liver trouble and had nearly died. Now she was up and about, running a health food store. She let me stay with her family, and I rode to the seminar with them.

The lectures sometimes lasted till midnight. Though I was exhausted, they helped clarify my thinking. It finally dawned on me I needed to go back to the Standard Macrobiotic Diet. Lino had told me to eat broadly and recommended spaghetti and pasta. I'd go to an Italian restaurant and have spaghetti with tomato sauce, riccota cheese, raw salad, and wine. To me that was eating widely. My understanding was wrong. He also told me to take pumpkin seeds with sea salt to strengthen the ovaries. He may have said a teaspoon of pumpkin seeds, but I thought he said a teaspoon of sea salt. I ate it, but it affected my heart, and I thought I would die.

I had also been taking some of Muramoto's herbs, which were too contracting. At home, I had been using chemically treated water and was told if I'd use this mixture on my gums, it would heal them. Instead it turned my teeth brown. In a panic I went to the dentist, and he cleaned them as best he could. I had lots of anxiety.

The workshop in Houston restored my direction. Bill Spear was energetic and a good speaker. He ran the macrobiotic center in Middletown, Connecticut. He emphasized that the Standard Macrobiotic Diet was a diet to maintain daily health, not a temporary regimen. It finally got through to me that I should return to the standard diet and begin cooking with spring water once again.

After Michio's workshop, I decided to see for myself if I could get well with just what's recommended in the standard diet—without any special concoctions, herbs, supplementary vitamins, digestive enzymes, carrot juice, or spirulina (a powdered algae). However, I couldn't eat pressure-cooked rice at this time. Either my condition or the climate was too yang. It was almost a year before I could eat it again on a regular basis. Instead, I had boiled rice or had rice soups. One big help was Mountain Ark Trading Company, which had just started in Fayetteville, Arkansas. I was able to get good quality miso and other staples by mail for the first time. Many macrobiotic foods that are taken for granted in Boston, San Francisco, or Los Angeles simply weren't available in Dallas. I started eating well again when I got back to Dallas and began for the second time to try to heal myself. And while I still had very little energy, I made cooking my highest priority. I'd cook seaweed, whole grains, and some vegetables and beans or other protein early in the morning. Then if I didn't have the energy to stay up, at least I'd have some food cooked that I could warm later in the day.

The food situation improved, but finances were still a big problem. Even if I'd had the energy, I had no clothes to work in and no money to buy any. And while my family sent money temporarily, it went for essentials—food, rent, and utilities. I had qualified to practice as a licensed professional counselor in Texas, but I didn't have any clients or money to secure an office space while I built up a private practice. I asked everyone I knew about work, and finally I was offered a job getting a house ready to rent. I went to the thift shop and bought a pair of Levis for a dollar so I'd have something to work in. The job turned out to be pulling nails out of the wall on my hands and knees. They had remained in the wall when the carpet had been pulled out. It was a cold, rainy day, and there was no heat in the house. My bones ached from the cold and the awkward position. The man who hired me could see that I couldn't hold out to do this work and made me another offer, but not one I was inclined to accept. I took my hard-earned $10 and went home.

In Irving, I applied for part-time work at a temporary secretarial service. They sent me around to various assignments, and I made $5.50 an hour. I had difficulty keeping my energy up and couldn't stay warm. On one assignment, as a typist for I.B.M., I had only my boots from Santa Fe to wear with a cotton denim skirt to keep warm in the cold office. I also wore them to cover up my legs. I didn't want to wear hose, nor could I afford to. Also I wore little make up and didn't have a permanent. The other woman in the office wore expensive clothes and always looked well manicured and coiffeured. The last straw was that I brought strange-looking containers of grains and vegetables to work for lunch. My stay at I.B.M. was short-lived even though my typing skills were excellent. I guess I didn't fit in with their corporate image.

An analysis of my financial predicament in early November showed I was over $5,000 in debt. The doctors' bills that had not been covered by insurance, including the anesthesiologist's, came to $1,600. And back in July, while still spaced out on sea minerals and shiitake mushrooms, I had been attracted to a pretty table and chair set made of hard-

rock maple at Levitz, a fashionable furniture store. I reasoned
that the dinner table was one of the most important objects
in a macrobiotic household, and I wanted mine to be of the
highest quality. What really sold me was the child's chair,
which was perfect for Jon. Also, the table was round just
like my family used to have in Munday. Because of good
credit ratings I'd established earlier, it was easy to reactivate
the credit from years back and have the set delivered to my
apartment. I also felt I would soon regain my health, be
happily teaching cooking and counseling friends, and could
easily pay for it.

I also thought in the back of my mind that Lino would
come back. He told me that I needed more feminine things.
For the bedroom I bought some expensive sheer drapes
decorated with roses, a very elegant mauve bedspread, and
a heart-shaped pillow covered with lace. For the living room
I picked out an off white cotton Haitian sofa and embroidered
throw pillows and a centerpiece made of shells, all in the
form of spirals. Before I knew it, I owed Sanger-Harris, a big
Dallas department store, another $1,600. Finally, I ordered
a cherry bedroom suite from Sears which cost several thousand dollars more, but in an enlightened moment had it
returned to the store.

Just before the surgery, I'd borrowed a thousand dollars
from the Texas Teacher's Credit Union to help pay rent,
groceries, and gasoline while I was off work. Unfortunately,
I wasn't able to return to work and someone else had to be
found to fill that position. It was an unbelievable shock to
find that I had absolutely no money. There'd never been a
time since I got out of college that I'd had absolutely no
money, nor could I see anyway to attract any. It was a dismal
situation. In late autumn, I applied for emergency food stamps
and received $75 for that one month. And worst of all, I
was alone.

When I came back from summer camp the previous year,
I had followed the Aiharas' advice and let Jon stay with his

father. The apartment in Denton was much smaller than the adobe house we had been living in Santa Fe. There was no-where nearby for him to go outside or any friends his age to play with. I was very yang from living in the mountains, from the summer camp experience and travel across the country, and from eating sautéed dandelion root when I should've been eating fresh pears. I found it hard to put up with Jon's activity and youthful chatter. I told Joe in late August that Jon could live with him, and he brought me a new set of legal papers to sign that had been drawn up by his attorney. Neither of us felt it was fair for him to continue paying child support while Jon was living with him. I didn't want to give up custody—just remove the child support provision—so I insisted on a joint custody agreement.

I was suspicious of the first set of papers and refused to sign them, so Joe had some changes made and brought a second set for me to sign. There were a few things that looked as if they favored him, especially in areas giving him approval for Jon's medical treatment. Yet I felt strong enough that I knew I'd also have a say in anything pertaining to Jon's health, and I made sure Joe understood that too. But it wasn't until much later that I realized the full impact of what I'd signed. While in principle we shared joint custody and the agreement made much of our mutual duties and responsi-bilities, in practice it turned out Joe retained residential control over Jon. Now in order for Jon to live with me again, even part of the year, I discovered I needed Joe's approval, and of course he wouldn't give it to me. I had used very poor judgment.

I was crushed. One of the reasons I went in to surgery was to become a complete woman again. I wanted to find a nice macrobiotic husband who was sensitive to Jon's dietary and health needs and would thus be a spiritual father to him as well as have other children to balance his energy and make for a happy family.

My relations with my former husband were a constant

frustration. While I was in the hospital for surgery, he never brought Jon to see me or even called to see how I was. When I got out, I called Jon. I hardly had any strength to drive over and pick him up, and I had no energy or money to take him to ball games or amusements as did his father. Joe made it plain not to look to him for any help. It became clear that healing my son was going to be a long and lonely struggle. I would have to find emotional strength somewhere else.

Iron Bars and Silver Hearts

Shortly before my operation, I received a letter from Frank Salvati in Boston. Frank was in charge of the East West Foundation prison project and was in touch with hundreds of prisoners around the country who were interested in macrobiotics. A former mailman, he himself had become macrobiotic after years of suffering from hypogycemia.

One of the men Frank was in touch with was Neil Scott, a bank robber serving a life sentence in the state penitentiary in Huntsville, Texas. What made Neil's case unique was that he had terminal cancer of the colon and was trying to eat macrobiotically, but prison officials, including doctors and nutritionists, wouldn't provide healthy foods or let them be sent into prison.

In Boston, Alex Jack, the editor of the *East West Journal*, ran articles about Neil and launched a nationwide campaign among readers to obtain his release. With the closing of Alcatraz, Huntsville became the nation's most notorious prison. A federal judge had issued a report comparing the Texas prison to a medieval dungeon and called for sweeping reforms. Alex sent an investigative reporter to Huntsville, a couple hours' drive from Houston, to see Neil, but officials refused to admit him. The authorities' stand brought even more impassioned responses from the macrobiotic and holistic communities, and the governor, legislature, parole board officials, the Texas media, and other opinion makers were bombarbed with letters from around the country demanding Neil's release.

As one of the few macrobiotic cooking teachers in Texas, I was asked by Frank if I could help Neil or help find other resources. After recovering from my operation, I started writing Neil and made inquiries on his behalf. For a long time, he didn't even have an attorney. There was a woman in my cooking class whose cousin was a state senator in Austin, and I contacted him. Also I knew two people involved with the Health Freedom Council which had been fighting against the repressive Medical Practices Act passed in Texas the year before banning holistic and alternative medicine. I wrote Mark White, the new governor in Austin, and other officials and told them that if Neil were released, he could come stay with me until he had regained his health. As a terminal cancer patient, Neil was eligible for a medical reprieve but twice had been turned down. Following write-ups of Dr. Sattilaro in the *Saturday Evening Post* and *Life Magazine*, macrobiotics earned a nation-wide reputation for relieving cancer. Though he couldn't get brown rice or any whole foods in prison, Neil felt it offered his best hope of recovery.

As efforts to free Neil continued, I heard from another prisoner, Chuck Fai Goon. Chuck was born in China and had come to this country where he became a U.S. citizen and served in Vietnam in the Special Forces. In prison, he had come down with serious health problems related to Agent Orange and heard of macrobiotics. I was the nearest teacher to the Federal Corrections Institute in Texarkana, Arkansas, where he was being held. Chuck asked me to come and talk about macrobiotics to a group of men he had organized who were interested in Oriental philosophy and the martial arts. I couldn't go initially because I was still weak, but we began a long correspondence which eventually included some cassette tapes on the Order of the Universe and other aspects of macrobiotic philosophy. The tapes gave me a purpose, and I felt needed.

By springtime I felt strong enough to travel. A friend drove me the two hundred miles to Texarkana. I had never been to a prison before and was apprehensive. Shortly before arriving, I stopped and meditated to center myself. At the main gate, I was greeted by big searchlights and tall barbed wire fences. I began to wonder if I was doing the right thing.

Out front, I waited inside a comfortable lobby until Rev. Presley, the chaplain, met me. He was the group's sponsor and soon put me at ease. He waited while I was cleared by the guards. They had run a security check on me earlier and soon waved me through. The huge doors clanged behind me, and I was uneasy. Rev. Presley escorted me to the prisoners' living quarters near the chapel. There I met Chuck, a tall bespeckled young man with large features and smiling eyes. He introduced me to Jerry Zastera, one of the other prisoners with whom I was also corresponding. There were about fifteen or twenty men assembled. All races and ages were represented, from the early twenties to forty or fifty. The men seemed very happy that I had come and after the talk bowed in Oriental fashion to show their appreciation. We just started talking, and I wasn't afraid anymore. I could feel the men's calm vibration and felt secure in their presence. We passed some strange-looking men on the way to the chapel, and I had the feeling they could be violent if provoked, but there were none like that in the group Chuck had assembled.

I talked to the men about my own healing experiences. I told them about the Standard Macrobiotic Diet and the importance of cooking, and we talked about what they could do to change their direction in their present circumstances. The afternoon passed quickly, and they had endless questions which I answered as best I could. Afterwards, some more of the men started writing to me, and I would answer each letter promptly. Through Frank, I heard from prisoners in other parts of the country, and soon I was corresponding with a number of men on a regular basis. I put little silver hearts on

the envelopes and peace stamps. While part of my dream had
not come true, I was still a woman with a mission and felt
these men had been attracted to me for a special reason.
I envisioned them one day walking at my side, learning from
each other, and together spreading macrobiotics throughout
the world. I enjoyed their friendship and tried to encourage
their dreams and help them see the front and back of their
situation and a broader view. I tried to help them see themselves as the infinite beings that they are rather than outcasts
from society. And they encouraged and reassured me in
return.

From my visits and correspondence with prisoners, it
became apparent that most of the men were ordinary people
with a more adventurous spirit than others. Their extreme
behavior resulted, in most cases, from their imbalanced way
of eating. In a society that fails to understand how they're
trying to make balance, they get in trouble. With the dualistic
view that they're "bad" and we're "good" and without
understanding the relationship of food to behavior, the
standard approaches to rehabilitating prisoners—punishment,
religious and ethical instruction, job training and social
retraining—fail.

I conceived the idea of setting up a program to introduce
proper diet in prisons. I applied for funds to the Ford Foundation, hoping they might be interested in a new approach.
In my letter, I explained:

> I'm developing a program designed to humanize the criminal
> justice system by working primarily with the inmate population.
> This design has never been implemented in its entirety with any
> population. (It's so difficult to study the effects of diet on
> behavior because people are unwilling to change their eating
> habits unless motivated by extreme conditions.)
> This multi-faceted approach will involve dietary change, inter-
> personal skill training, exposure to traditional approaches to
> physical fitness, and religious/philosophical teachings.
> I plan to implement this to some degree with or without grant
> assistance. Yet alone I would feel like a flickering 10-watt bulb

trying to light a vast cavern of darkness while with the giant
torch of a Ford Foundation grant, I could breeze confidently along
the most precipitous passageway.

I received a polite reply that I needed nonprofit tax status
to apply. I didn't even have the money to apply for that, so I
persevered in simpler ways. The *East West Journal* sent me
four boxes of old magazines, and I took about 300 of them to
a federal prison in Seagoville, Texas, a suburb of Dallas. They
were well received by the head of the education department
there. I went to see Neil Scott in Huntsville and returned to
Texarkana for a second talk.

Some of the men I corresponded with had colorful names
like Rainbow, Jewel, and Kabir, and by and large they were
very gentle and sweet. But others had very strong opinions
about religion, government, and prison issues and would
write volumes to me about their ideas. For awhile I exchanged taped cassettes with a man in California on death row.
But when he chastised me for practicing macrobiotics (on a
tape cassette that he shared with all his other correspondents),
I stopped "talking" to him.

It may be coincidence but many of the men I was writing
to are now free, including one who had been in prison for
twenty years and had been turned down for parole time
and time again. While visiting Neil, I stopped to look
through the prison store. I wanted to buy something hand
made. The leather belts and purses didn't appeal to me so
much, but foraging through a box of paintings I found a
sensitively drawn pencil sketch of a long-haired woman
holding an infant. I tried to buy it, but there was no price
tag, and the man who ran the store for many years was
absent that day. The clerk filling in was unwilling to set a
price on it. There was nothing left for me to do but write the
artist whose name was inscribed on the picture. He then sent
the picture to me as a gift.

Charles, the artist, didn't have a dietary philosophy but

had given up meat several years before after becoming violently ill on some he had eaten in prison. The principles of balance afforded by macrobiotics made sense to him. We began a regular correspondence, and he was paroled within a few years. It's true that I wrote some letters in his behalf, but more importantly is that our correspondence kindled the fire of his dream to be free.

Chuck Fai Goon, who had invited me to introduce macrobiotics at Texarkana, also had a happy ending. After being transferred to Powhattan State Penitentiary in Virginia, he started a macrobiotic study group there which developed into the largest macrobiotic prison project in the country. Some of Frank Salvati's co-workers at the Kushi Institute in Boston traveled to Virginia and prepared a macrobiotic banquet in the prison. Four hundred men attended, and the acting warden changed his way of eating. By this time, Chuck himself had already been released. He came up to Boston to study macrobiotics and teach traditional Chinese medicine and the martial arts. He now has his own office and a thriving practice.

In another situation, the justice system has been less sympathetic to one of the men I was in touch with. He remains locked up. However, I was able to introduce him to one of my macrobiotic friends in Dallas, and now they're married and enjoying conjugal visits.

In one way or another, everyone I met or wrote to enriched my life, bringing new meaning and forcing me to explore my values. In a letter to Frank Salvati, I summed up my overwhelming positive experience working with prisoners and told him how they had become part of my planetary family:

Now in writing to these prisoners I begin to see a new need —to have another direction. It's wonderful. And they are remarkable. In spite of the fact that many of them have been in dreadful environments, they still seem to have more vitality than those 'on the street.' And they're into many different things—theology, music (many into music and I can't read a note!), astrology, poetry, Kung Fu, Tai Chi, stress reduction, and on and on. In addition, they've had so little female attention that they are most appreciative.

So many times with the macrobiotic men I've met, I have felt as if they focused so much on my 'condition' —that I felt diminished by them. I just felt like they were seeing my mucous congestion or weak ovaries, or this or that, instead of the real me—the infinite being that I am (that we all are). With these guys, they think I'm wonderful and I revel in their attention. . . .

One of my dreams is to have my son with me again. . . . He lives with his father who is remarried. We divorced before I changed my diet and life. Fortunately, everything changes. Until it does though I will spend my time on our special friends. They are like sons to me in spite of their ages. I think it has more to do with their situation and needs. I'm beginning to feel like the old woman who lived in the shoe and I love it.

Giving Shiatsu

In Oak Cliff, Sebastian, the gay drifter who moved into my house, continued to be a thorn in my side. He now had a job and had stopped eating meat and sugar. He even asked for brown rice to take in his lunch. But his heart was not into learning how to cook himself, and he joked about becoming "a macrobiotic queen."

After Christmas, I felt it was best to ask him to leave. I figured if he lost one home he'd attract another, and I'd attract someone else. Shortly after, Doug Caswell, a young man from Nebraska, turned up. He had just started macrobiotics and had come to Texas looking for work. I offered to cook for him and teach him what I knew, and he could share the apartment and help with the rent.

Doug mentioned that Michio did personal guidance for his students by mail. I wrote to Boston explaining to him how weak my intestines were after the surgery. He wrote back recommending that I eat fish or seafood two to three times

a week, as well as tempeh and natto frequently, and some
fresh salad. It was the first time I'd eaten fish since becoming
macrobiotic, and I immediately began to feel stronger.
Michio's advice meant a lot to me. I'd spread his letter on
the floor and read it from time to time. He sent his very best
regards and made me feel special.

One night I joined Doug and a friend of his for dinner in
hopes of expanding my job prospects. He worked for an
alternative weekly, the *Dallas Observer*, and suggested I
place a classified ad in it and begin building a shiatsu practice.
Shiatsu is the traditional acupressure massage of the Far
East. It is based on a deep understanding of *ki*, or natural
electromagnetic energy, flow through the meridians of the
body and has been used therapeutically for thousands of years.
Shiatsu is taught in many macrobiotic centers, and I first
studied this healing art with Ken Burns at the Aiharas'
Summer Camp in Northern California.

I felt shiatsu was a good way to share information about
diet while supporting myself. I ran a classified ad in the
Observer and printed up brochures for the Shiatsu Study
Center of Dallas. The first person who came was a middle-
aged businessman. It was all I could do to bend over and
press my hands along his back. I had no strength. I had lost
my confidence and self-image. But he seemed to respond to
my touch, however feeble. The work strengthened me, and
my energy started to come back.

Over the next several years, I built up a successful practice
and gave many massages. As I grew stronger, I noticed that
some of the men felt the approach was too hard and preferred softer Western-style massage.

Shiatsu taught me a lot about health and sickness, especially
diagnosis. Most of the men who came to see me were heavy
meat eaters. Their whole bodies were tight from years of
eating too much steak, hamburger, hot dogs, chicken, and
eggs. Besides the muscles, joints, and skin, their inner
organs were hard, and the energy through the meridians was

often blocked from these foods as well as from cheese and dairy food. Just from lightly touching certain pressure points, I started to learn what organs and systems were stagnated or weakened. And I could feel lumps of cholesterol and fat along the meridians.

Most of the men who came had heart problems. Their faces and ears were red from high blood pressure. Their breath was short. They were very yang—ambitious, successful, wealthy. Those with swollen noses, especially those with purple at the tip from expanded capillaries beneath the skin, were prime candidates for a heart attack. They called in the middle of the day, 10 A.M.–2 p.m., the hours when the heart, according to traditional Far Eastern medicine, is most activated. Others would call early in the morning, when the liver is most stressed, and one man invariably called from 4 to 6 P.M., and sure enough he had pancreas troubles. I came to know when to expect certain people to call.

I had studied Esalen massage while in Santa Fe and integrated some lighter techniques into my treatments. I talked to some of the men about diet and the need to change their way of eating, but most of them weren't interested in understanding the cause of their problems. They wanted just quick relief from their symptoms. Occasionally, I'd have someone vegetarian or macrobiotic to work on. That was such a joy. In comparison to the meat eaters, their bodies were softer, suppler, and more flexible.

While I worked, I would visualize myself sending energy and love to my clients and cleansing their auras. When they continued to eat badly and came back with the same probblems, it was very discouraging. There were a few who changed. One man went on the Pritikin diet and lost 42 pounds. That was encouraging. And one or two others stopped eating meat and found they didn't miss it. I hoped that more would remember someday my advice. Sometimes I'd offer them something to eat, or they'd smell the food cooking in the kitchen and say, "What is that?" And when I'd say,

"That's barley and beans," they'd say, "I wonder where that dish came from?"

I resumed giving macrobiotic cooking classes when my strength returned but with a certain amount of anxiety as it's illegal to give any dietary advice in Texas unless you're a physician. I never knew if someone (a medical doctor, for example) was coming for a cooking class to entrap me or out of genuine concern for his or her health. But I kept the classes small and relied on my intuition, and everything worked out OK.

Like any traditional craft or art, shiatsu taught me a lot about yin and yang and the infinite Order of the Universe. The work had a big back and big front. Some people thought I was the lowest kind of person and yet others held me in the deepest respect.

"No Guts, No Glory"

During the two years following surgery, my strength began to return. I was still weak by ordinary standards, but I began to reach out and share my experience and insights with other people. The early part of the day I devoted to shiatsu. In the afternoons, I walked in the park, and in the evenings I would write or make cassettes for my friends in prison.

Just ten minutes' walk from my house in Oak Cliff, Kidd Springs Park was my special place of refuge. Its twelve acres held a large eliptical fishing pond, outdoor swimming pool, baseball diamonds and tennis courts, and a rec hall with inside basketball court. But for me the greatest attraction was the Oriental Garden. Through a small archway, the path spiraled uphill past beautiful flowers and shrubs to a Japanese shrine. The shrine was constructed in the Shinto style with long sloping roof and heavy beams finished in red lacquer. It was very calm and peaceful. Like the small stone Buddhas on one part of the hillside, I liked to meditate and look out over the sea of humanity below me—families picnicking,

children playing ball, lovers strolling hand in hand, and old
men fishing.

Like a dot in the yin/yang symbol, the garden was a touch
of the Far East in the center of the Wild West and a re-
minder that everything contains the seed of its polar opposite.
Someday, Dallas—the center of material wealth and excess,
the steak-eating capital of the country, and the heart disease
hub of the world—would become macrobiotic. It was as
inevitable as day following night and the mountain rising
up from the valley.

In the spring of 1984, I met Duncan Echolson and Maki
Tsubota. Duncan had been studying macrobiotics in Japan
for several years. Maki had studied with Lima Ohsawa at the
Nippon C.I. in Tokyo and with the Kushis on a trip to
Boston. They met in Japan, married, and came back to
Dallas where Duncan's parents lived. In addition to a family
that grew to include three bright, happy children, Duncan
and Maki started Universe Distributing Company, a macrobiotic food business that supplied natural foods stores in
Dallas with the staples and specialty foods that had long been
unavailable.

Maki gave some cooking classes. She taught me to use the
less salty misos in the winter (such as *kome*) and the more
salty ones in the summer (such as *mugi*). She explained we're
more active in the summer and need to sweat and replace the
salt we lose. I was doing it the other way. Plus I was taking
in too much miso according to the traditional way they
measure miso in Japan (by the size of the finger to the first
joint).

Then I'd seldom been able to use grated *daikon* because it's
so pungent. But Maki let hers dry in the sun for a day or two
and used only the middle part for eating raw and in pickles.
She used the ends in soups and cooked them longer. After
studying with her, I liked daikon a lot better.

Earlier that year, I had decided to try to get Jon back. I
could see the fat building up in his little body from cheese,

milk, ice cream, meat, and eggs. His intestines had swollen, his muscles had hardened, and energy blockages were beginning to spread throughout his body. If he continued to eat the modern diet, he could have cancer or cardiomyopathy by his early twenties. I felt I had been insane to give him up.

I talked to Joe and Diana at New Year's about taking Jon back, and they said to wait until school was out. I didn't want to wait and went to a lawyer. He wanted $5,000 to take the case. I went to Legal Aid and found an attorney. She was very sympathetic and said that she would request a hearing. She said there was a chance I could get custody back.

However, in the middle of filing, she left Legal Aid, and I was assigned a new lawyer. He was totally unsympathetic. He told me I had no legal basis to get my son back. He said circumstances needed to be changed. I couldn't believe that I had no right to even request a hearing. I told him I was healthier now and could take care of Jon and I felt that was enough of a change in circumstances. I brought him material on macrobiotics and scientific and medical papers on children whose conditions had dramatically improved with proper nutrition. But they seemed to have no more effect on him than they did on Joe or Jon's doctor. He became belligerent. I wondered whose side he was on.

As the legal proceedings mired down, I tried another approach. I devoted myself to starting a natural foods business. I wrote to Frank Salvati,

> I want my son to grow up knowing what whole grains are and taste like and feel like. If I have to put in a store so he can have that experience, then I'll do it . . . I'm already writing to distributors to get wholesale information on foods. It's my nature to plan ahead. It's going to be funny if this stream of salesmen start appearing at my door and I don't have the money yet. Ha! Well, no risk, no gain. Or as they say crudely in Texas, "No guts, no glory."

As summer approached, my strength faded, and I couldn't attract any investors. I had to put off my dream of a natural foods shop until another season. Meanwhile, Joe's attorney came back with threats that I was unsuited to take care of Jon. Then seeing me with Jon at a ball game seemed to soften Joe, and he called and asked if we could talk once more.

Joe came over and we talked things out. I told him if he would cook brown rice for Jon, I would drop the lawsuit. I tried once again to explain about yin and yang in foods, and I explained why Jon had gotten so skinny living with me in New Mexico. I told him that I hadn't been practicing macrobiotics accurately then and felt I could do better now. I told Joe I just didn't want Jon to grow up thinking his mother didn't want him. Joe said he would cook brown rice for Jon. By the end of our meeting, we were both in tears.

I dropped the custody hearing. I didn't feel comfortable about going the legal route either. I cared about Joe and his family too and wanted to have a good relationship with them. In letters to Frank Salvati, I wrote, "My deep feeling is that we are all on the same side in this—although on the surface it seems his Dad and I are opposed . . . I believe everything else will change in time once they start eating brown rice. It did for me."

For awhile, Joe lived up to his side of the agreement and cooked for Jon. But it's hard for a man to work, cook, and do everything else. I realized I was making it worse for Jon by constantly pushing and pulling him in different directions and asking what he'd had to eat. Like a lot of kids whose parents were fighting over them, he was caught in the middle, trying to please both mom and dad. "Have y'all had that court thing yet?" he would ask anxiously. It became clear that I must develop patience.

Back to Boston

That spring Neil Scott was paroled from Huntsville. How he

survived six years with terminal cancer (and later tuberculosis) is one of the wonders of modern medicine. Even though he couldn't get natural foods, he used macrobiotic principles and techniques, such as ancient Taoist liver exercises, to bring his tumor into remission. He spent some time in North Dakota where he had been paroled to work on the farm of a Seventh Day Adventist family.

That summer, Neil arranged with his parole board to move to Boston. The Seventh Day Adventist way of life (which ironically he had grown up in) was too narrow for his tastes, and rural North Dakota was not very exciting. In Boston, Alex Jack helped arrange for Neil to go to the East West Foundation summer camp in the Berkshires and receive a scholarship to study at the Kushi Institute. Neil invited me to join him at the summer camp. When I looked on a map of the States, it seemed such a long way off, but one day I saw a map of the world and it seemed much nearer so I agreed to go.

I managed to scrape together enough for a plane ticket to New England. Like dozens of other people, I worked in the kitchen in exchange for attending summer camp. It was wonderful to be in the Berkshires among so many macrobiotic friends and see the Kushis again. Neil still seemed really yang—tight, impatient, on edge. But who wouldn't be after being in a Texas prison for nine years and living through what he did?

I attended a talk given by Haruo Kushi, Michio and Aveline's son. He had just received his doctoral degree in nutrition from Harvard. For years there had been a controversy about how much Vitamin B_{12} vegetarians or macrobiotic people needed. Haruo cited recent scientific research showing that it exists in fermented foods such as miso and tempeh as well as in animal foods. He warned, however, that overexposure to the sun could contribute to a B_{12} deficiency as could drinking carbonated beverages, fruit juices, and too much strong yin or strong yang. In another workshop, Bill

Spear explained that the more yang vitamins tend to concentrate in the core and skin of vegetables. It was important to eat the whole plant, including these parts. "If you cut off the top of a carrot or apple," Bill said by way of example, "you cut off the connectedness between heaven and earth."

I also sat in on some natural beauty classes with Luc Bodin. Originally from France, Luc had studied with the Kushis and for a while operated his own hair salon in the Back Bay. He explained how most commercial cosmetics contain animal products and are toxic and showed us how to use simple foods, plants, and other natural substances to keep our skin healthy and beautiful. For ordinary cleansing he recommended an oatmeal ball. You make this by filling a cheesecloth with oatmeal, dipping it in water, and then using it to wash the skin. He also showed us how to prepare a home-made facial sauna, a moisturizer and after shave, an oil to use after a bath, massage oil, and shampoo.

Denny Waxman, a senior macrobiotic teacher from Philadelphia, gave a stimulating class on diagnosis. He had helped Dr. Sattilaro heal himself of terminal cancer, so I knew he was an experienced diagnostician. He talked a lot about the energetics of food and explained how excess accumulates in different parts of the body. Meat, which is very yang, tends to go downward, collecting in the rear end, the large intestine, and the ovaries or prostate. Cheese, a more yin form of animal food, collects in the thighs. The mid-section bulges out in many people, Denny continued, because of too much simple carbohydrates, including white flour, sugar, alcohol, and fruit, causing this area to loosen. Meanwhile, dairy food, including milk, butter, ice cream, and sour cream, as well as sugar, accumulates in the upper part of the body, especially the breasts in women, and in the throat. Chicken goes to the back, particularly to the area between the shoulder blades. As I listened to Denny's talk, I realized I still had some old chicken in me as my shoulders were still tight, not to mention a few other foods in other places.

Another lecturer I enjoyed was Murray Snyder, director of the macrobiotic center in Baltimore. I had received a consultation from him and respected his balanced approach. He encouraged me to stick to the Standard Macrobiotic Diet, with appropriate adjustments and modifications, and did not recommend any exotic supplements or special kind of salt or minerals. Murray's talk at summer camp was devoted to another aspect of energy flow. He distinguished between two kinds of *ki* or natural electromagnetic energy: 1) *outside ki* that comes from the planets and atmospheric conditions and 2) *inside ki* which comes from our daily food. He explained that if we take in too much *ki* from the outside, our blood quality becomes very thin. Conversely, when we eat too much, our nervous system becomes dulled from too much *ki* on the inside and we become less sensitive to the vibrations of the invisible world. It was important to keep a dynamic balance between these two forms of nourishment.

The Summer Camp's main speaker, of course, was Michio, and he would lecture for two to three hours every morning or afternoon. The camp's theme was "Macrobiotics—Passport to Peace and Health," and Michio devoted his main lecture to the threat of bionization—the rapid artificialization of bodily organs and parts—and genetic engineering. He said that the natural human species was dying out on this planet. Unless modern civilization returned to a more natural way of life, including way of eating, it could die out within several generations from AIDS, cancer, heart disease, infertility, mental illness, and other degenerative disorders. He said that nearly everyone was unaware of this danger because all the attention was focused on nuclear weapons. World war was the more immediate, yang threat to our survival. However, human life could also end in a slower, more yin way as we lost our health, judgment, and ability to reproduce naturally.

In a lecture on spiritual development, Michio talked about the next world—the world of vibration and spirit. He said that there is no hell except for what we create ourselves in this

life. "Hell is what you create by your delusions. You need
not be afriad when dying if you have been eating well. You
will experience a peaceful, natural death. The quality of our
consciousness at death determines our happiness in the next
life. Even three days eating macrobiotically before death
makes a big difference and can lead to a smooth transition to
the world of light." For years I had been troubled by the
images of punishment and retribution in the after-life I had
been brought up with in church and Sunday school. Michio's
clear, peaceful description of life and death and his teaching
that eventually everyone returns to God or One Infinity was
tremendously reassuring.

At summer camp I also met Alex Jack for the first time.
Alex had left the *East West Journal* to write *The Cancer-
Prevention Diet* with Michio, and I was interested in talking
with him. The last day of camp, Neil and I caught a ride to
Boston with Alex. However, I was so tired, I slept the whole
way back in his car and hardly exchanged greetings.

Following My Star

Back in Dallas, some words in a summer camp brochure
stayed in my mind—"Whatever you can do or dream you
can, begin it. Boldness has genius, power, and magic in it."
I thought of returning to Boston and continuing my studies
at the Kushi Institute. However, I had no money and didn't
want to be so far away from my son. But I took careful mental
note of my surroundings—the carpeted stairs, the long table
and windows looking out over the Berkshires, the fireplace
and cozy den—knowing that if I could envision it in my
mind, I could return to it.

That fall, Neil notified me that he was going to write a
book. Alex had helped him get a contract from Japan Publications to write about his healing experiences in prison. He
said he would be working on the book full-time and couldn't
use the scholarship at the K.I. and would give it to me
instead.

The offer of the scholarship was like an answer to my prayer. I decided to accept Neil's offer and move to Boston. Neil and I were good fiends and he reminded me a lot of my brothers. I wanted to cook for him while he wrote his book and rebuild his health and dream.

The idea of moving up North excited me. I hated Texas's oppressive heat. And Dallas is such a sprawl. It took me all day just to go shopping. You have to be somewhat yang to survive, especially when trying to be both male and female, that is, earn a living and cook, clean, and take care of the house. But because of the hot, yang environment, everyone in Dallas gets extremely yin. Your energy is always drained and your activity is dispersed. I much preferred a smaller, colder place to live. Also, my abdomen was still very tender from the surgery, and I felt it would heal better in a four-season climate. Being so far away from Dallas would also increase the polarity with Jon and might make it easier to attract him back.

Meanwhile, my financial problems reached a crisis. The trip to summer camp was expensive, and my shiatsu practice fell off while I was gone. My car got ill, and Sears presented me with an $800 bill to fix it. I had paid off the doctors and the teacher's credit union, but all other credit card payments were in arrears. People were bugging me to death about their money. I had been able to return the cherry bedroom suite, but Levitz wouldn't take back the dining room set. Altogether I owed $3,500, which wasn't that much. But I was worn down. I had no money to go out to eat more than once every several months. I had traded my air conditioner to the land-lord one month in lieu of rent. Another time I sold him a beautiful oval table for a pittance. In the fall, I decided to declare bankruptcy and filed the papers myself since I couldn't afford a lawyer.

I gave notice to the landlord and packed up everything at home in cardboard boxes. Each time I earned a little money, I'd mail off a box to Boston. Neil planned to support me when I got up there while I cooked for him and went to school. He also said he'd pay somebody to drive my car up north since I was too weak to do it myself. He sent me some money once to help buy an airline ticket. I found a college student ready for adventure and willing to drive my Dodge Colt up to Boston.

In Boston, I discovered Neil was having a difficult enough time on his own. I arrived with the image in my mind that I wouldn't be working there, and I wasn't immediately prepared to change it. When I lost my billfold, it seemed like I lost my identity along with it. I had nowhere to stay, no money to go home, and no home to go to if I did.

Alex Jack heard of my plight and invited me to come over and talk at his apartment in Brookline. He was just finishing writing a book on diet and heart disease with Michio and a macrobiotic cookbook with Aveline. Divorced a few years earlier, he understood perfectly my difficulties with Joe and Neil. Over bancha tea, he said that if I didn't mind sharing a home with three macrobiotic cats, I could stay in the extra bedroom. I moved in, started cooking and we have been together ever since.

12.

The Great Life

Ladies to the center, back to the bar
Gents to the center make a Right-Hand star.

I T'S BEEN OVER TWO YEARS NOW since I left the K.I., six years since the last surgery, and over nine years since I began trying to practice macrobiotics (or "the Great Life," as the term means in the original Greek). It has been about ten years since I've eaten any beef, pork, ham, chicken, cheese, or milk as a source of protein. I ate an egg once when a girlfriend from Dallas visited me in Santa Fe and was sick the whole day. For the last five years, I haven't found it necessary to visit a doctor or purchase any over-the-counter drugs, not even an aspirin.

I haven't had a yeast infection since 1979. On two occasions I've had severe bladder discomfort and went for acupuncture treatments to relieve the symptoms while I made the necessary dietary adjustments. Kidney/bladder problems can be caused by taking in too much salt, which leads to the excessive intake of too many desserts (even naturally sweetened ones), fruits, fruit juices, and fruit spreads such as apple butter. I've also found atmospheric conditions to be a factor when I have kidney/bladder problems. Usually my symptoms occur in a damp, cool month.

The last time I saw an acupuncturist, I was questioned extensively by his wife. "Have you been drinking Cokes?" she asked. "No, I don't drink Cokes." "Have you been drinking coffee?" "No, coffee makes me sick. I can't drink it." "Sugar?" "No." This continued until we finally hit upon something sweet that I'd been eating. Then she said, "Why did you eat that?" as if I should have known beforehand not to eat it. Well, now I do. But sometimes I can take in more yin and sometimes less, and I don't always know until afterwards that I took in too much. I'm still learning. But she was from Thailand and (judging by her condition) brought up on a traditional diet. She knew intuitively that what I had eaten had caused the problems that brought me to their office.

Then during the treatment, I asked her husband if I had taken in too much salt, and he said, "Yes, too much salt." After three treatments, some ginger compresses and hot baths at home, and a week of eating well, I was OK and have had no recurrences.

The really wonderful part of the physical improvements in my condition is that they've gone hand in hand with an improvement in my mental and nervous functioning. Fifteen years of visiting psychiatrists, psychologists, and social workers and of attending therapy groups ended when I changed my way of eating. I had spent thousands of dollars and hundreds of hours trying to communicate my needs and insecurities to professionals as well as studying different approaches on my own trying to find the cause of my own behavior in addition to that of others. And much of that time was spent trying to figure out how to change other people to meet my expectations rather than accepting them and helping them realize their own dreams.

I'm embarrassed to admit it, but long before we separated I used to fight with my husband all the time, even scream at him. And I'd sometimes curse and always feel badly about it later. I complained about everything he did and wanted to run his business and mine. I didn't like many of his friends and seldom felt like socializing anyway. I was depressed for almost a year following the birth of my son. I was always spending money on clothes and things for the house without any regard for what he might need.

From my experience I now know that selfishness, depression, fear, greed, prejudice, jealousy, forgetfulness, and a tendency to argue or fight are all related to diet. After thirty-five years of eating animal food, I began to lose my human quality and spirit. From so much chicken and eggs, I would sometimes act like a chicken, running around without any direction and hen-pecking my husband. From so much beef and hamburger, I would act like a bull, charging out of the house, making money and wielding power, and neglecting my home and family. But I was one of the lucky ones. Somehow I was able to return to a more natural way of life and restore my health and happiness. Call it intuition, providence, or the voice of God, I was led back to the traditional way of eating of my parents, grandparents, and ancestors.

Whole Grains and Grain Products

The diet that I follow is based on whole cereal grains. When I first heard this term, I wondered, "Is it like the brown rice I get from the supermarket?" Actually whole grains are now available in many supermarkets, but those are often grown with chemical fertilizers and pesticides. Organically grown grain is regularly found only in natural foods stores or through macrobiotic mail-order suppliers such as the Mountain Ark Trading Company in Fayetteville, Arkansas.

Whole grain, still the principal food in most traditional societies today, should constitute about 50 to 60 percent of our daily food intake. Brown rice generally forms the basis of the macrobiotic diet. I eat it every day. It's the most balanced food and naturally sweet. I use it as a standard to compare other sweet tastes. For example, compared to the natural sweetness of brown rice, chocolate pie, Hershey bars, and other desserts that I used to eat made with sugar, honey, and maple syrup taste icky sweet. Sometimes desserts made with grain sweeteners such as barley malt or rice syrup taste too sweet too, but these are much preferable to simple sugars and are generally balanced products if taken in moderation.

I often eat brown rice for breakfast as a soft cereal, cooked with 3 to 4 cups of water per cup of rice and a pinch of sea salt. Rice prepared this way is very easy to digest. I eat brown rice for lunch sometimes and almost always have it for dinner. Brown rice can be pressure-cooked, boiled, steamed, or roasted. It is my staff of life. My brother M.J. loves to tease me when the family meets at a restaurant. He glances over the menu and says, "You can't eat here. They don't serve brown rice." I do eat out now without fear of getting sick, but I do miss having brown rice as the center of a meal. Sometimes, instead of salt, I cook it with a small piece of kombu seaweed, which is rich in minerals. Eating whole grains as the center of the meal makes menu preparation so much easier than when I cooked the usual modern way.

Barley and millet are the two other grains I use most often. For some reason I have difficulty eating millet by itself. I don't feel so good in a few hours. But I enjoy millet cooked with cauliflower, butternut or other hard squash, summer squash, or in combination with other grains such as rice or sweet rice and rice. I often enjoy barley by itself in a soft cereal or in soups. It seems to be one of the easiest grains for me to digest. I also sometimes cook it with rice. Certain kinds of barley cooked with rice yield a nice sweet taste that's a pleasant variation from rice cooked by itself.

In the winter I occasionally cook whole oats for breakfast or with rice. I use rolled oats—ordinary oatmeal—all year long. I grew up eating oatmeal and still enjoy it two or three times a week. I like to dry-roast it in a skillet for about 5 minutes before boiling. That gives it stronger energy and a nuttier taste. I use fresh corn when it's in season—boiled on the cob or cut off the cob to use in a variety of ways. *Masa*, whole corn dough made from organic flint corn, is sometimes available ready-made from the natural foods store or can be made at home and is delicious in tortillas, arepas, and corn waffles or used in soups.

Whole wheat, cracked wheat, and bulgur are harder for me to digest so I don't use them often, but they do add variety.

From time to time, I enjoy unyeasted sourdough breads but find these are more difficult to digest than whole grains. I usually eat them accompanied by miso soup. I feel clearer when I don't eat bread at all.

Mochi—pounded sweet rice—is one of my favorite foods. I cook it into waffles or heat it on top of the stove and eat it with tamari soy sauce and grated daikon and sometimes with nuts, barley malt, or occasionally some kind of fruit spread. I also like to add it to soups. Mochi is very delicious and strengthening. It's often recommended for new mothers. I wish I had known about mochi when my son was nursing. Now it is one of his favorite foods.

I use corn grits, a Southern favorite from time to time, usually for breakfast or in addition to another grain. I especially like grits with pinto beans. And polenta is nice cooked with onions, fresh corn, or other vegetables. One other grain that I've learned to enjoy is couscous. Steamed in an equal amount of liquid (half apple juice and and half water, for example), it makes a light and tasty dish. This can then be topped with boiled vegetables or some type of fruit prepared with agar-agar.

Only in the last couple of years I've begun to enjoy a variety of noodles as part of my diet—*udon, soba, somen,* and others. They're easy to prepare, easy to digest, and delicious besides. Children seem especially fond of noodles.

In general, it is recommended that about four-fifths of our daily grain intake be composed of whole grains and about one-fifth or less of our grain eaten in the form of noodles and bread, cracked cereals, flaked cereals, oatmeal, couscous, and grits.

Some people recommend less that 50 percent whole grain in yang (hot) climates, but I've found that causes me to lose my direction. Mild spices can be added to rice in a warm climate on occasion, but too many spices cause nervous problems, irritability, and forgetfulness and more attraction to sweets to calm down.

Soup

The Standard Macrobiotic Diet recommends 1 to 2 small bowls of soup every day, accounting for about 5 to 10 percent of daily food by volume. When I first changed my way of eating, I didn't use miso soup—the most popular soup in macrobiotic cooking—very often. I felt it was too salty and was making me too yang. And the way I prepared it, it was. But over the years I've found it's hard to eat well without it. Miso—made from fermented soybeans, often barley or rice, and sea salt—has so many important functions that I think it would benefit almost everyone. A small bowl of miso soup at the beginning of the meal aids digestion. Very yang in nature, miso attracts and stimulates the yin digestive juices in the stomach that help metabolize the food. It also is filling and keeps us from overeating. (Overweight people especially will appreciate miso soup once they've learned how to prepare it properly and experienced the benefits.) Miso also contains amino acids and certain vitamins and minerals that aren't readily available elsewhere. If I eat one bowl of miso soup prepared with vegetables from sea and land, I feel I have received more nourishment than in three full meals without miso soup.

There are many different types of miso. For daily use, I like to have a barley miso that's aged 18 months or longer. Then I like to have other lighter misos (red, yellow, and white) around for sauces, dressings, warmer days, and simply to vary the tastes. Please experiment for yourself, and don't feel you have to eat the same miso every day for the next three years or that you don't like miso soup after having tried it once. Though miso itself is salty, the soup should not taste salty. The soup should actually have a slightly sweet taste if properly prepared. If it tastes salty, chances are you're using too much miso. If you're more attracted than usual to sweets, fruit, salads, and other yin foods during the day, it may also be because the soup is too strong.

For variety, I sometimes prepare other soups, including tamari soy sauce broth, lentil or bean soup, or vegetable soup with a variety of fresh vegetables. If I'm tired in the evenings and want something light, I'll often prepare a rice soup and eat that in lieu of a large meal.

Vegetables

About one-quarter (25 to 30 percent) of our daily food ideally includes vegetables prepared in a variety of ways—steamed, boiled, pressure-cooked, sautéed, water-sautéed, and so on. It's very important to include some lightly cooked vegetables each day such as steamed or boiled greens, a boiled salad or, if your condition permits, a raw salad. Otherwise, even eating just grains and vegetables, you can easily become too tight (yang) and be attracted to foods that are much more relaxing (yin) than the ones you tried to avoid, such as desserts made with sugar, alcohol, and excessive fruits and juices.

Among the stem/root vegetables recommended in the macrobiotic diet (such as burdock, carrots, daikon, dandelion root, lotus root, onion, radish, rutabaga, turnip, and parsnip), I can use only a few. Burdock makes me incredibly tense. The last time I ate it, I got extremely aggressive and was ready to charge off and tell someone off. Fortunately, I've had enough experience now in seeing how food affects my emotions that I didn't do it. I just gave the house a good cleaning instead and had some warm apple juice later. Used in small amounts, it can aid digestion and promote sexual vitality.

Dandelion root affects me about the same way. Lotus root makes my lungs tight, and I usually cry after taking it. However, I like to use lotus root as medicine. When I have a sore throat or sinus congestion—which I usually get every fall— I fix some tea made from lotus root and eat a tiny piece or two with the tea, and the soreness is soon relieved. Sometimes it will take two or three days. The real purpose of the macrobiotic way of eating is to help us regain our natural intuition so that we know which foods we have to avoid and which ones will make us feel more peaceful and balanced and even which home remedies are the most ideal for our constitution and condition.

I enjoy all of the usual ground vegetables recommended such as cauliflower, acorn squash, buttercup squash, butternut squash, Hubbard squash, Hokkaido pumpkin, and pumpkin. Among the leafy green vegetables that I have almost every day, I enjoy broccoli, Brussel sprouts, bok choy, green cabbage, Chinese cabbage, collard greens, turnip greens, kale, mustard greens, parsley, scallion, chives, watercress, leeks, and daikon greens. I still find it difficult to eat carrot tops and dandelion greens.

In the summer, I use celery, cucumber, lettuce, sprouts, snow peas, green peas, summer squash, and string beans regularly. I don't care much for zucchini (it's too watery for me), eggplant, green or red pepper, Swiss chard, sweet potatoes, or spinach. Early in my macrobiotic practice, I enjoyed sweet potatoes occasionally but now find them too sweet and mushy to be satisfying. All potatoes make my stomach puffy.

When I first began practicing macrobiotics, I had the feeling that the diet was something macrobiotic teachers wanted to impose on me and that these restrictions were not necessary in my case. Since my constitution was yang and since I lived in a yang climate, I felt I needed more fruit, less cooked foods, and wider variety. To some extent this was true. I could have enjoyed more fresh salads and fresh fruits for awhile and later did add those to my diet. Even now I can take in more fruit and some fruit juice during the summer, but after about a month of eating this way I notice that my intestines become swollen and my digestion is not so good. And on a rare social occasion I've eaten some small pieces of tomato or a salad with a vinaigrette or lemon juice dressing only to find myself breaking out in a rash a few hours later or in an embarrassing itch.

I have finally concluded that the macrobiotic dietary guidelines were given not to restrict me but to ensure my happiness. Based on the way our ancestors in both West and East
ate for many generations, they were arrived at by those who
had eaten these foods before and come to know—long before
I did—the effects they have on health, mentality, and behavior. After coming to the United States, Michio and
Aveline Kushi gradually developed the standard macrobiotic
dietary guidelines in harmony with environmental conditions
and personal needs in North America and other temperate
climates. In the beginning they made many mistakes too, and
year by year, season by season, their recommendations
continue to evolve. The Kushis have shared their understanding and insights with us so that we can restore our
health and happiness. It's in the same spirit that I now
share my experiences with you.

Many of my friends think that I follow a very narrow diet.
It is limited in the sense that among the total population, very
few people follow it, but it is broad in the variety of foods
that are included and the wonderful meals that can be prepared with them. My way of eating before I became macrobiotic was one hundred times narrower than the way I eat
now. Not only had I not tasted many of the grains and
vegetables, but also I had no idea how to make them. Though
my mother had cooked "a mess of turnip greens" and other
greens frequently in my childhood, I didn't know how to
prepare them. I didn't know what butternut or buttercup
squash was and had never even made a pumpkin pie. I didn't
know much about cooking at all. I just had a few basic dishes
that I prepared for company and, as a member of the fast
food generation, literally ate on the run—a barbeque sandwich here, a cheeseburger there, an order of chicken to go.
I ate lettuce and tomato salads, potatoes, and some beans but
didn't care much for other vegetables.

I have found that the study and practice of macrobiotics has
immeasurably broadened my diet and that I now enjoy many
vegetables, in addition to other foods, that I once avoided or

didn't even know existed. By the same token, I've found it best to avoid some of the larger, more yin vegetables such as asparagus, spinach, avocado, sweet potato, green and red peppers, tomato, yams, zucchini and Swiss chard. Occasionally, when the full moon approaches or I find myself getting too yang for some reason, I will cook an Irish potato and find it helps me relax.

Beans and Seaweed

My diet includes about 5 to 10 percent beans and seaweed. For daily use, I prefer azuki beans, chickpeas, green lentils, and black beans. I occasionally add black-eyed peas, kidney beans, great northern beans, split peas, red lentils, pinto, lima, and navy beans, but find the latter more difficult to digest. Since my kidneys tend to be tight, I cook azuki beans with squash or serve them cooked with raisins, chestnuts, or barley malt. The sweet flavor keeps them from making the kidneys tighter. Fermented bean products such as tempeh, dried tofu, and natto add variety to a diet and are easier for me to digest than other beans. However, I'm not much on raw tofu. In spite of America's recent attraction to tofu as a good-quality source of protein instead of meat or dairy food, I find it too high in fat for regular use. It remains on the list of occasional use food in my family. My son likes it deep-fried and seasoned with tamari soy sauce which is also the way I prefer it.

Sea vegetables were also new to me when I began practicing macrobiotics. Prior to that time, the only one I had tried was kelp powder, which is about as appetizing as powdered cardboard compared to properly prepared seaweeds. Now I regularly use kombu when cooking beans and put it on the bottom of *nishime*-style vegetable dishes, and from time to time prepare it as a dish by itself. Wakame is easy to use cooked in soups and with carrots and other vegetables. It has a relatively mild taste. Sea palm is nice and tender. I prepare it similar to arame, and enjoy it with corn-on-the-cob, with carrots and onions, or with tempeh. I like to have nori on hand at all times. It's easy to fix in condiments, to use with rice balls and sushi, to cut up as a garnish for soups, and to roast as a snack by itself. Agar-agar is nice for aspics and gelatin molds, but when you're my age you have to be careful about eating cold desserts, even those made with good quality ingredients. It's better to eat them at room temperature. The only seaweed that I don't use often is *hijiki*. Actually I like its taste and texture, but again it makes me very yang, so I usually only eat it in small amounts and with light seasoning. Early in my macrobiotic practice, the seaweeds I made never tasted good, but when I'd eat those other people cooked they tasted great. I finally found that I wasn't cooking them long enough—especially hijiki. Hijiki needs to be well cooked.

Supplementary Foods

I sometimes use white-meat fish or seafood once or twice a week. Recommended ones are flounder, halibut, sole, cod, carp, haddock, trout, clams, oysters, smelt, scallops, *chirimen iriko* (tiny dried fish), and *chuba* (small dried fish). Once when *koi koku* (carp soup) was recommended, I substituted red snapper instead. Trout can also be substituted. Fresh oysters and smelt are hard to find; in fact, fresh fish of any kind is hard to find in my area. I can sometimes find cod, sole, or haddock, so naturally I use those more often. I almost never eat the small dry salted fish. The excessive energy they give makes me feel most uncomfortable.

Nut butters are my weakness. I know they're high in fat and oil and hard to digest, but I grew up eating them, and it's a hard habit to break. When I have an emotional upset, sometimes nothing will do but a peanut butter and jelly sandwich. Little by little, I'm learning to substitute whole roasted nuts such as almonds, walnuts, seeds and chestnuts when available. I roast these and season them with tamari soy sauce or sea salt.

My favorite dessert is squash pie. I also enjoy cooked

fruit desserts once or twice a week, sometimes sweetened with rice syrup or barley malt or apple juice with kuzu. During the hot summer months, I have fresh raw fruit and melon on occasion as well as organic apple juice from time to time. I usually drink the apple juice mixed with an equal part of water. It tastes too strong by itself, and adding the water dilutes the apple juice, as well as brings its temperature up, especially if it's been in the refrigerator. In the summer, we usually have fresh peaches and blueberries. They make a nice dessert. Sometimes I serve cantaloupe and blueberries. Almost every guest can appreciate these desserts. We also have a variety of grapes and can sometime get nice plums and cherries. Pears are often available, too. I minimize the use of strawberries because they seem too acidic, but Alex loves them and seems to handle them all right. In general, there's no difficulty getting a variety of fruits. The problem is limiting their intake.

I sometimes make crust-less squash pies because making a crust is still difficult for me and also because I like to avoid eating desserts made with oil and flour. Sometimes I'll top a blueberry or apple crisp with roasted, slivered almonds instead of the traditional "crisp" topping of flour, oil, salt, rolled oats, and nuts.

Beverages

I always use fresh spring or well water in preparing tea and in cooking unless well water is available. For daily use, I use bancha twig tea (*kukicha*), roasted rice tea, roasted barley tea, or water. I occasionally use grain coffee and, in the summer, find *umeboshi* tea refreshing. However, *mu* tea and dandelion tea give me a headache. I've never been able to drink them. I used to drink carrot and celery juice in large amounts, but when I drink them now, which is seldom, I find an ounce or so is sufficient. Also I usually add a little spring water to vegetable juice because the taste seems too strong by itself. I've also found that more than a small amount makes me cold. I do enjoy a small amount of beer on a hot day. Again, my family grew up drinking beer. But I never drink it in the same large amounts they did. Instead of a six-pack in an afternoon, I drink a small glass or share a bottle with someone. My brothers used to put a small amount of salt around the edge of the beer can and drink it that way —a intuitive method of trying to balance yin and yang.

Condiments

Besides providing additional nutrients, condiments make the food more palatable, especially for people who have recently been on a diet high in salt and other minerals. Too, since each family member needs a different amount of salt and minerals based on his or her age and amount of physical activity, condiments allow individual family members to balance their intake. One of the mistakes most newcomers to macrobiotics make is in their overuse. If you're excessively thirsty within an hour or two after a meal or eating a half a jar of apple butter between meals, you'll know you're going overboard. With condiments available, I feel comfortable cooking with very little salt without making the meal tasteless for others. The following are some of the condiments I enjoy:

Tamari soy sauce: I use this mostly in cooking. It's very contracting so I've found it best not to use it on rice or noodles at the table and in moderate amounts during cooking.

Sesame salt (gomashio): This is made from roasted sesame seeds and sea salt ground together in a small earthenware bowl called a *suribachi* until about two-thirds of the seeds are crushed. For adults, fourteen to eighteen parts sesame seeds to one part roasted sea salt is the usual proportion. For children and the elderly, up to twenty-five parts sesame seeds to one part salt can be used.

Roasted seaweed powder: Roast wakame, kombu, dulse, or kelp in the oven until crisp (about 350 degrees F. for ten to fifteen minutes) and crush in a suribachi.

Sesame seed powder: Use four to eight parts sesame seeds to one part kombu or wakame and prepare as you would gomashio.

Umeboshi plum: Plums that have been dried and pickled for over one year with sea salt are called *ume* (plum) *boshi* (dry) in Japanese. On the average, adults may eat two to three plums per week. Umeboshi stimulates the appetite and digestion and aids in maintaining an alkaline blood quality. They help bring the body back into balance if you've eaten too many sweets. They're easier to take if you pour hot water over them, then drink the water, and eat the plum or part of it.

Sesame seed, vinegar, and miso condiment: Another condiment I especially like is roasted and ground sesame seeds prepared with rice vinegar and miso. The vinegar adds a sour taste which is nice.

Sauerkraut: Traditional sauerkraut is made from cabbage and sea salt. A small amount can be eaten occasionally by adults and older children. Cooking the sauerkraut with tempeh or seitan or serving it just by itself is nice. The sauerkraut can also be eaten raw but is stronger that way.

Vinegar: A small amount of brown rice or umeboshi vinegar can be used from time to time by adults and older children. Apple cider vinegars are best avoided.

Seasonings

It's important to use some oil in cooking unless you have a serious condition, and even then you should only avoid it temporarily. Oil makes food very delicious and satisfying so that you aren't inclined to eat as often. Sautéed vegetables several times per week and occasional deep-frying of grain croquettes, vegetables, and fish and seafood adds greatly needed variety to the diet. If I don't sauté vegetables for several days or have any deep-fried food, then I find myself attracted to nut butters which are much harder to digest. For the past several years, I've used only light sesame, dark sesame, and corn oil for the majority of my cooking. Once in a while I try some olive oil for a change and have enjoyed rice bran oil when I could find it.

Salt is important to balance oil and make it digestible. I use naturally processed, unrefined sea salt. Regular table salt that you buy in the store has many additives and dextrose, a type of refined sugar.

The use of seasonings and condiments can vary so much from person to person that it's very important for each person to study cooking and diagnosis and then practice self-reflection daily to determine how much he or she needs at any given time. We can't blindly take one, or one and a half, teaspoons of any given seasoning or condiment a day just because other people do. But the guidelines are important in the beginning; otherwise we might start with three tablespoons instead of a teaspoon or less.

Way of Life Suggestions

There is an order in the universe and it extends to all areas of life—not only to how we cook and take our food (although that is the most important area for us to know and exercise order)—but also to where we live, what kind of house we live in, where we sleep, what we wear, what kind of daily activities we chose, and how we relate to family members and others in society. I'll mention a few macrobiotic way of life suggestions and give you some examples from my own experience.

1. Chewing your food thoroughly is essential. Whole grains can be chewed 100 times. The less food we have, the more important this becomes as proper chewing is essential to obtain needed energy and nutrients. Also for

people who are in situations where they cannot obtain the best quality of foods (such as schools, prisons, hospitals, and other institutions), chewing is very important. To really change your condition, take two bites of grains to one bite of vegetables or other side dish. Don't mix grains and vegetables in the mouth.

2. It's important to eat only when hungry and not snack all the time as it interferes with digestion and with eating more balanced meals.

3. Eat in an orderly manner. At mealtimes, we should eat from yang to yin, taking the miso soup and any animal food at the beginning of the meal. Whole grains may be eaten from beginning to end, even with dessert. Vegetable dishes may be eaten along with the grain, followed by desserts and tea if desired.

4. Avoid long hot baths or showers, as these drain minerals from the body. However, if you've been taking in too much salt or animal food, then bathing in this way is a nice way to relax and may be especially important for women.

5. It's better to leave the table feeling satisfied but not full. For mental activities, you can eat to about 80 percent of your capacity.

6. It's best to avoid eating for three hours before sleeping. Going to bed shortly after eating creates stagnation in the intestines, leading to poor digestion and absorption and then excess accumulation in the body.

7. Scrub and massage your entire body with a hot damp towel until the skin becomes red, every morning and/or night, to activate the circulation and the flow of energy

throughout the body. Scrubbing the hands and feet is the next best thing. Begin the body scrub with the feet.

8.   It's best to wear only cotton clothing next to the skin as it allows the skin to breathe and sweat more easily. All of those years that I was having yeast infections and chronic bladder problems, I was wearing nylon hose and nylon undergarments. Substituting silk hose is not a good idea either. It's best to use simple, natural jewelry as much as possible and avoid heavy metal rings and bracelets.

9.   Going to bed and getting up early is more natural than going to bed and getting up late. I used to have a great deal of difficulty getting out of bed in the morning and would reset the alarm several times and have to be prompted by my mother or husband to get up. Then when I did get up, I felt tired. In the past few years I wake rested and feeling good nearly all the time and ready to work at whatever I'm doing that day and don't find it necessary to use an alarm clock.

10.   Every day, we should make the beds, sweep the floors, put away clothes, and in every way make order in the home. Once a few years back when I was thinking about coming to Boston to further my studies, I wrote to a friend, "I've prayed (contemplated the Order of the Universe), meditated, and read Ohsawa and others . . . but I think my greatest insights come when I'm mopping the floor."

11.   We should spend some time outdoors every day even in winter. When the weather is mild, we should walk barefoot in the dirt or grass to make contact with nature. I love sitting under big trees when I read or write letters. I feel so much more a part of the universe when I do.

12.   It's best to use natural materials in the home. Cotton futons, sheets and pillowcases, cotton towels, and cotton or

wool carpets all make the home feel softer and more natural. Natural wood furnishings, wood floors, and/or cotton and wool carpets make a softer and more natural home environment. Also, pastel (lighter colors) in the home are much more relaxing than the vivid blues, greens, and other bold colors popular with many professional decorators.

It's best for the woman to make the decisions regarding the decor of the home. Both partners can choose the house itself, but the interior decorating should be left to the woman as much as possible. It's her center. She spends more of her time there and is more affected by its vibrations—especially the bedroom.

When I separated from my ex-husband, one of the first things I did was to take down the orange drapes he had picked out, put up some soft green ones, and change the bold orange spread to one of nice mellow colors that I could live with. For the first time in years, I felt as if I could relax in the bedroom. Had I done that earlier, the relationship might have gone differently. The effect of the home on a woman cannot be overemphasized.

13.   It's best to use a gas or wood stove for home cooking rather than electric or microwave cooking devices. Food cooked with wood or gas is much more peaceful and harmonious than that cooked with electricity or microwave. Over the years as I've changed homes, I've always chosen one with a gas stove or had one installed.

14.   Minimize the use of electrical appliances next to the body such as electric razors, hair dryers, stereo headsets, electric blankets, heating pads, toothbrushes, toys, etc.

Earthware, cast-iron, enamel, or stainless steel cookware are preferable materials for cookware. Aluminum or teflon-coated pans should be avoided.

15.   Keeping large green plants in each room in the house

will brighten the atmosphere of the home, provide oxygen, and help you feel like you're a part of nature. Plants are very soothing to nervous functions. Open windows daily to let the air circulate even in cold weather. I don't see how people can live in large, beautiful homes and never open the doors and windows for air to circulate. Actually, they don't live as long or as happily when they insulate themselves from the environment. To a visitor, the house often smells stale or like hair spray, lysol, or laundry detergent. You become more sensitive to different smells when you're eating natural foods.

16.   The use of television can be minimized. Color TV is best avoided, not only because of the effects of radiation (it is much more tiring to the eyes), but also because it is so addictive and limits the time we have to spend in other activities that help strengthen the family. These include playing the piano or other musical instrument, singing, reading (either silently to oneself or out loud to others), playing games outdoors, play acting, building things, sewing, crocheting, quilting, and knitting.

Women's Health Recommendations

Female disorders have risen sharply in recent years. Every year more than 700,000 American women have hysterectomies. At that rate, about half of the women in the country will have their uterus or ovaries removed by age sixty-five. The variety of sexual problems ranges from premenstrual syndrome to vaginal discharge, blocked Fallopian tubes, breast and ovarian cysts, fibroid tumors, and cancer of the breast or reproductive organs.

To understand these problems, we need to look at the cycle of menstruation and ovulation. During the first half of the menstrual cycle, between the woman's period and ovulation and beginning of the period, the hormone progesterone predominates. The length of time taken for each stage in the cycle depends largely on the woman's way of eating. If she eats primarily whole grains and cooked vegetables, menstruation usually takes only three days. However, among women who eat a diet high in meat, sugar and dairy products, five or six days is the average. The next phase, in which the endometrium (the lining of the uterus) regenerates itself, usually takes two days. However, with proper eating, this can be accomplished in only one day. The following stage, in which the follicle matures, lasts about eight days, and ovulation should occur in the part of the cycle that is exactly opposite to the onset of menstruation or, ideally, fourteen days. In healthy women, conception usually takes place at this time or four to five days after ovulation. During this phase, the yellow endocrine body (corpus luteum) found in the ovary in the site of the ruptured follicle matures and secretes progesterone. This hormone influences the changes that take place in the uterine wall during the second half of the menstrual cycle. The follicle and corpus luteum eventually decompose during this phase if not fertilized and are discharged during menstruation.

If a women is eating properly, her menstrual cycle should correlate with the monthly lunar cycle, or about twenty-eight days. During the full moon, the atmosphere becomes very yang—bright and charged with energy. A woman who regularly eats grains, cooked vegetables, and other centered foods and is physically active will usually menstruate at this time. The condition of the atmosphere will cause her to become more energized, necessitating the discharge during her period. During the new moon, the atmosphere is darker or more yin. Women who menstruate at this time are usually eating a more expansive diet—more fruits, salads, sweets, and so on. After eating properly for some time, a woman begins to menstruate around either the full or new moon, indicating that her condition is in harmony with the natural atmospheric and lunar cycle.

During the first half of the menstrual cycle, women quickly

regain balance and can readily follow a more centered diet of whole grains, cooked vegetables, and seasonal fruit. Immediately prior to ovulation, fertility is expressed with general feelings of joy, contentment, and bliss. The woman usually feels terrific, remains cheerful and confident, and her eating stays centered during the few days of ovulation.

During the second half of the cycle, as menstruation approaches, some women become dissatisfied and irritable and may eat constantly or cry easily. Overcooked foods, animal food, and other heavier dishes may become unappealing and if taken in excess frequently lead to the overeating of sweets, fruits, salad, and liquid. In such cases, just prior to menstruation, some women may experience tenderness and swelling in the breasts and a general bloated feeling. They may continue to crave strong foods in the yin category and to feel impatient and melancholy. The pharmaceutical industry capitalizes on Premenstrual Syndrome by offering various products to help balance this condition, but with proper dietary adjustment, drugs aren't necessary.

In order to have a smooth menstrual cycle, it is important for a woman to adjust her diet during the two halves of the month. During the first two weeks, between menstruation and ovulation, she should eat plenty of dark, leafy green vegetables along with whole grains and other more substantial foods to which she will be naturally attracted. During the last two weeks, between ovulation and menstruation, she will feel more comfortable if she reduces her intake of overcooked foods and avoids animal food altogether. Otherwise they will produce an increased craving for sweets, fruit, juices, salads, and lighter foods. To prevent this, she should eat more lightly cooked vegetables along with lighter seasonings and less salt. Special dishes such as mochi, turnip or radish tops, or amasake will help reduce cravings for more extreme foods.

An irregular menstrual cycle results if the diet is too imbalanced in one direction or the other. For example, if it totals less than twenty-eight days, this usually indicates an

overly yang condition from eating too much animal food or
other foods high in minerals or food that has been overcooked. A cycle longer than average, up to thirty-two or
thirty-five days, shows that a woman may be eating too many
foods in the yin category such as sweets, fruits, and dairy
food. Both conditions can be corrected by eating a more
centered diet of grains and vegetables.

Menstrual cramps are usually caused by an excessive intake
of meat, fish, eggs and dairy food (especially cheese) in
combination with too many expansive foods such as sugar,
soft drinks, refined flour, milk or ice cream, and chemically
processed foods. Cramps can be eliminated in two to three
months on a balanced standard macrobiotic diet.

Excessive menstrual flow can result from overeating
either too many foods from the yin or yang category. In the
case of too much animal food rich in protein and fat, the blood
thickens and the flow lasts longer. This is often accompanied
by an unpleasant odor. When too much extreme yin is taken,
including food that slows down body metabolism, the blood
becomes thinner than normal and menstruation is prolonged.
When a woman eats a more balanced diet, menstruation will
be of shorter duration and the flow will be lighter. Biologi-
cally, women need not eat any animal food but if desired, they
can occasional have very light white-meat fish such as cod or
shellfish.

Deposits of fat and mucus, coming largely from animal
foods, dairy foods, sugar, and refined flour products, often
accumulate in the inner organs if an imbalanced way of eating
continues over several years. In women this buildup tends to
concentrate in the breasts and in the uterus, the ovaries, the
Fallopian tubes and the vagina. The solidification of mucus or
fat around these organs can result in the development of
cysts and tumors.

The accumulation of excess in the breast often results in a
hardening of the breasts and the formation of cysts. Excess
usually accumulates here in the form of a sticky or heavy

liquid. These deposits develop into cysts in the same way
that water solidifies into ice, and the process is accelerated
by the intake of ice cream, milk, soft drinks, fruit juice, and
other yin foods that produce a cooling or freezing effect. Cold
or icy beverages in particular should be avoided.

Cysts that occur in the comparatively tight ovaries are
saturated in quality or yang, whereas those in the more
expanded vagina or vulva are of a more yin quality and
contain more fat and mucus. Most cysts are soft when they
begin to form, but with the continuation of an improper diet
they harden and often calcify. This type of cyst is very
difficult to dissolve. Some varieties of cysts contain fat and
protein and can become extremely hard, in which case they
are called dermoid cysts. Tumors represent the final stage in
this process as the body attempts to localize the continuing
influx of unhealthy nutrients by creating blockages and
obstructions in various organs and sites of the body. The
accumulation of fat and mucus can also block the Fallopian
tubes, preventing the passage of egg and sperm and resulting
in the inability to conceive.

Cysts and tumors can be created by various combinations
of foods including milk, cheese, ice cream, and other dairy
products; sugar, soft drinks, chocolate and other sweeteners;
fruit and fruit juices; nut butters; greasy and oily foods;
refined flour and pastries such as croissants, doughnuts and
sweet rolls; hamburger and other animal foods. Once again,
serious mammary or reproductive illnesses may be relieved
by eliminating extreme foods and centering the diet on
whole grains, miso and other soups, beans, vegetables, and
sea vegetables and, if craved, small volumes of cooked fruit
and seeds. As the condition improves, a wider form of the
standard macrobiotic diet can be adopted.

Recently there has been a sharp increase in herpes and
other sexually transmitted diseases. Generally, these afflic-
tions are caused by a long-time way of eating that is too
yin. Foods such as sugar, sweets, tropical fruits and vege-

tables, refined flour, and milk, ice cream, and other light dairy products weaken the blood. A multitude of viruses and other microorganisms lives in symbiosis inside of us and usually will not give rise to disease unless our blood quality is weakened. If our blood quality is strong, our body's immune system will neutralize any harmful bacteria, viruses, or other organisms. People who eat a balanced diet and strengthen their blood and immune system over a period of time and limit their physical relationships to others who are eating well don't need to worry about getting infected with herpes or AIDS.

Childhood Recommendations

One night in Santa Fe I kept a lonely vigil at Jon's bedside, a vigil begun some forty hours before. How suddenly things had changed. One day he had an occasional hacking cough, and now spasms racked his little body, making breathing difficult and sleep impossible. Following one such spasm, his head dropped lifelessly to the pillow, and he looked at me with his beautiful, deep blue eyes and said simply, "I'm dying."

The icy fear that gripped my heart choked away any reassurances that I might otherwise have had for him. Nothing that I or anyone else had done for him in the preceding days had given him any relief. Exhausted and near tears myself, I lifted him gently from his bed and carried him to mine, hoping to share my Life Force with him. Holding him close, I drew the comforter over our shoulders (as much to warm the cold within as to shut out the wintry chill) and began to pray and meditate on the Order of the Universe.

During the six months that passed since my consultation with Michio in Boston, I made many errors in cooking for Jon, as beginners often do. But it was one of the most wonderful periods of my life—to be at home cooking and spending time watching and being a part of Jon's develop-ment rather than feeling compelled to go to an office everyday. We had so much fun together, and for the first time since he'd left his father, he began to laugh again—a spontaneous, deep laugh which lightened the whole room and warmed the hearts of those who heard him.

And now to have him facing this crisis—to be so weak and so near death (so it seemed to me) was incomprehensible. I tried every remedy I knew to ease his coughing. Finally after 3 A.M., his coughing finally eased, and I drifted off to sleep with the words of my mother on my mind, "It's always darkest before the dawn."

I woke before Jon and took time for further self-reflection. A few days before, we had visited friends in the country. Not knowing exactly what we ate, the hostess had bought bananas and apples and prepared a large pitcher of orange juice. Jon accepted a large glass of orange juice, and I didn't interfere. The discharge began soon after.

The proper care and feeding of children has been a big issue in the macrobiotic community, and I don't suppose there is any easy answer or consensus how to bring up children in modern society. No one wants their kids to be exclusive, nor do they want to have to stand over them with a club to see that they eat well. But my own situation reminded me of the woman in Boston whose youngster developed rickets. The girl had started stealing apples from the store, and yet the mother had missed the cue just as I did. Children need yin! And if an ample quantity of good quality yin is provided for them or kept within their reach, they're much less likely to steal apples or drink 10 or 12 ounces of orange juice or whatever else might be offered them once away from home. Also, I've found that children need much less salt than we do —perhaps one tenth as much. And they require more vegetal protein since they are growing and building more new cells. Fewer baked products are appropriate since baking is yang-izing—in spite of our tendency to want to nourish them with our cookies and other pastries—and noodles are nice.

Another mistake occurred when Jon's symptoms had reached the point that neither of us was getting any rest. I was in a

hurry to have the symptoms abated so we could get on with
our lives (a rational goal on the surface), so I took him to a
local acupuncturist for treatment. Alas, the treatment accelerated the symptoms instead of relieving them. But for some
reason I was unable to communicate my need in this situation,
or even if I did, the man remained adamant that his line of
treatment needed to be pursued. So I learned two lessons:
1) what appears to be the slowest way to health (and happiness) is often the fastest and 2) it's not always wise to put
someone else's judgment higher than your own. In fact, it's
dualistic to think that everyone else is in tune with the
Infinite and has a corner on Truth while we ourselves are
ignorant. It's not humility but duality that leads us to seek
advice hither and yon while not relying on our own intuition.

Contemplating these things, I cancelled the appointment
with the acupuncturist (much to his chagrin) and set aside all
remedies recommended by him and well-meaning friends:
comfrey root tea, osha root cough syrup, honey, lemon, and,
yes, even Vick's salve. Children generally need only the
slightest amount of treatment. I prepared a warm ginger
compress and laid it across Jon's chest, then crawled back
into bed with him. For the next 24 hours, I rubbed and
patted and held and reassured him that he would be all right.
Sometimes I rubbed the lung points, sometimes his back or
the kidney area, sometimes points around his toes. Following
my intuition, I rubbed gently here, more firmly there, sometimes just leaving a hand on him as he slept. Occasionally
he offered guidance, "No, rub here," and so on. Except for
an occasional venture into the kitchen for soft rice and
steamed greens, this is how we spent all day Saturday and
Saturday night.

Then Sunday morning at dawn, I woke to the sound of a
Nerf ball bouncing against an adobe wall. Soon a small face
appeared at the bedroom door, "Mom, I'm hungry!" Though
I don't recall what grains and vegetables we had for breakfast
that morning, I'm sure they were jumping with joy.

13.

Planting my Feet on Higher Ground

I'm pressing on the upward way,
New Heights I'm gaining ev'ry day.
Still praying as I onward bound,
Lord, plant my feet on higher ground.

Lord, lift me up and let me stand,
By faith, on Heaven's table-land,
A higher plane that I have found;
Lord, plant my feet on higher ground.

AFTER CHANGING MY DIET AND WAY OF LIFE, my understanding of religion and spiritual practice changed. Growing up, Jesus was considered the son of God, and like other Southern Baptists we worshiped him and sought salvation from our sins. With this kind of philosophy, you never get the feeling that you're OK. You're always in the process of trying to find favor with God but never feeling as if you are already a child of the infinite universe.

One of the songs that we used to sing reflects this very well. It's called "Higher Ground" and is quoted at the top of this chapter.

Now my feeling is that we have to plant *our own* feet on higher ground. And the way that we can assure that we'll be on high ground tomorrow is through the food and activities that we choose today. If we eat well today, spend time with our friends trying to understand them, and spend time outdoors and in mental activity such as writing or meditating, our life automatically comes into balance. We gain higher ground by adapting our life to the order of nature or the universe, not by some lord smiling down on us.

Another song we sang was, "I Surrender All." It went:

All to Jesus, I surrender,
All to Him I freely give;
I will ever love and trust Him,
In his presence daily live.
I surrender all, I surrender all;
All to Thee, my blessed Savior, I surrender all.

Perhaps this attitude of surrender is beneficial at times, but to think that someone else is our savior and master is to misunderstand Jesus's own teachings.

All of these songs imply that you can break God's law and yet call upon someone outside yourself (in this case Jesus) to save you from your "sins" and restore your health and happiness. In my experience, this is untrue.

Our only hope for health and happiness in this life is to be fortunate enough to be attracted to a teacher of the Order of the Universe or through despair come to reflect, study, and change our own direction. After studying macrobiotics, I began to realize Jesus's true teachings. Since I was a small girl in Sunday school, I had always puzzled over the story in in the New Testament of how Jesus fed the multitudes with two small fishes and five loaves of barley bread. Was it simply a miracle or was there some reason for his using just that amount of food?

I now realize that the two small fishes symbolize yin and yang—the passive and active forces that make up the relative world. The five loaves of bread signify the five phases of transformation, which are a further refinement of yin and yang. In the newly discovered Gospel of Thomas, Jesus refers to these principles directly. "If they ask you: 'What is the sign of your Father in you?'" Jesus tells his disciples, "Say to them: 'It is a movement and a rest [that is, yang

and yin].' " He also discusses "the five trees in Paradise"
whose knowledge brings eternal life. Thus in the familiar
Gospel stories of feeding the multitude, it is clear that Jesus
is not just feeding the people physically or performing a
supernatural feat. He is teaching them the order of nature and
the universe. He is instructing them in the universal laws of
change and harmony. These, of course, include dietary principles of balance. Everywhere in the Gospels Jesus distributes
whole grain bread—the staff of life to his followers and
supplements his own way of eating with vegetables, fruits,
seeds, and some fish. Nowhere is he described as eating
meat, poultry, or dairy food, and it is well known that except
for fish the earliest Christian community was vegetarian. In
his teachings and in his way of life, Jesus was completely
macrobiotic.

This was an amazing discovery. Rediscovering the true
meaning of the Gospels, I began to look back at my religious
upbringing with new eyes. There was certainly a lot of chaff
but also some wheat mixed in. One of the songs I liked,
Count Your Blessings, went like this:

When upon life's billows, you are tempest tossed,
When you are discouraged, thinking all is lost,
Count your many blessings, name them one by one,
And it will surprise you what the Lord has done.
Count your many blessings, see what God has done.

I realize now that what I liked about it was its intuitive
understanding of front and back, positive and negative, yin
and yang. The order of the universe includes both the good
and the bad, joy and sorrow. By embracing our illnesses,
difficulties, and disappointments, we become stronger and
more appreciative of life as a whole.

Another song I liked had a refrain which went:

Blessed be the tie that bind ours hearts in Christian love,
The fellowship of kindred minds is like to that above.

288

We sang this at the close of Sunday evening services following an evening of events that might have included a pot luck dinner. Although I outgrew the church's dogma, I learned that eating together and singing together do build ties that bind us together as one family and am grateful for that experience growing up.

Overcoming Violence and Hatred

Another tune I will never forget is "Jesus Loves the Little Children."

> Jesus loves the little children,
> All the children of the world.
> Red and yellow, black and white,
> They are precious in his sight.
> Jesus loves the little children of the world.

Although we sang songs like this in Sunday school, growing up I still felt uncomfortable around people who were from other cultures or of other races. This attitude lasted until I started to change my way of eating and include more whole grains in my diet. Then I was able to accept the people that I grew up singing about.

Prejudice, discrimination, and violence, especially to other races and religions, are still big problems in modern society. As children, feelings toward Blacks and Mexicans ran pretty high. My sister remembers being told to wash her hands after playing with an Indian.

In addition to the legacy of my father's death, I grew up amid a lot of violence and hatred. I don't know that it was really any worse or deeper than that elsewhere in the country. But in Oklahoma and Texas it was out in the open. It was not subtle or hidden as in some other parts of the country.

Like many young men their age, my brothers, cousins, and young men in the neighborhood were always getting into fights. Brawls, guns, knives, and other violent ways of settling disputes are a way of life in the Southwest. On several occasions, a family member or relation was sent to jail. One cousin went haywire over some girl and was sent to the state penitentiary in Oklahoma. As a little girl in Muse, I remember on a visit seeing him brought into the courtroom with chains on his legs, and he, in turn, was chained to other men.

Since becoming macrobiotic, I have gained better insight into the causes of violence and the forces that led up to my father's death. Briefly, hatred, aggression, violence, and other extreme forms of behavior are caused by a combination of imbalanced foods, especially meat, eggs, poultry, and other extreme yang foods, usually in combination with alcohol, sugar, or other extreme yin.

In my father's case, day to day the men at the poker table had all been eating too much animal food. That's why saloons and bootleg whiskey existed: to offset the extreme yang diet of the Wild West (beef, buffalo, and other wild game). Meat and alcohol stress the liver causing strong feelings to arise that we call anger, resentment, and hatred. Only a spark is needed to set off an explosion of accumulated metabolic energy or what we may call an emotional discharge.

Tragedies such as my father's death have happened countless times in American history. Now on a global scale, the nations of the world are playing poker armed with nuclear weapons. Like my Daddy and the Indian, they have abandoned their traditional diet of whole grains and vegetables. Their judgment has clouded, and the smallest spark—in the Middle East, Europe, or Central America—could destroy the whole world. It is all so senseless and unnecessary.

Ancestral Ties

Several years ago, on the way to Fayetteville, I took the scenic route and stopped to have lunch in a park in Mena, Arkansas. There was a log cabin, and I found a fresh spring running into the park. I visited for awhile there with an old-timer and found myself reluctant to drive on. I kept thinking what a nice place it would be to live.

Just recently I found out my grandfather and grandmother lived in Mena, and that's where my father is thought to have been born. I had always thought he was born in Oklahoma! I now realize my intuition—the voice of ancestral tradition— had led me there.

In preparation for this book, I have further traced my father's family back to Georgia. I have not been able yet to positively identify my forebears, but there is increasing reason to believe, as family legend has it, that my great-grandfather was an Indian and or was married to an Indian. Fields was a distinguished name among the Cherokees. A number of American Revolutionary officers and traders married Indian women and settled down in the southern Appalachians. According to early 19th century census records, the few Fields who lived in Georgia at that time were con-centrated in the Indian territory.

The Cherokees, like other mountain tribes, had traditionally been very yang and dominated the eastern half of the conti-nent. But in the long Indian wars with the French, British, and Americans, they lost most of their hunting grounds. Their heroic effort to save their traditional way of life has been recounted numerous times. Renouncing war, the Chero-kees turned to agriculture, the arts, and a democratic form of government. Sequoyah, their gifted prophet, composed an alphabet to preserve his people's culture and tradition. There was even talk of the Cherokee Nation joining the United States.

The Cherokees' traditional way of life was very balanced. Their tribal emblem was a Seven-Pointed Star, showing a deep understanding of the Order of the Universe and the logarithmic spiral. In courtship, the custom was for a young man to slay a deer and take it to the lodge of his sweetheart to indicate that he was a good provider. If she accepted his suit, she prepared it into a meal for him. But if she let the deer lie outside, he must take it back and find another spouse. In their lectures, Michio and Aveline Kushi have defined true love as the woman choosing to follow a man's dream and man agreeing to eat woman's cooking. In such things as their love of ballgames and field contests, I feel the spirit of the Cherokees has passed on to my son, Jon, whose love of sports exceeds even that of eating.

Despite their high culture, the Cherokees were completely dispossessed of their lands in the South in the 1830s and forced to resettle, first in Arkansas, and later in Oklahoma. Like the ancient Israelites, they were exiled from their own home and taken into captivity. Thousands perished along the Trail of Tears—the 800-mile wintertime journey they were compelled to make—including children, mothers, and grandparents.

The native people of this continent were divided and conquered as much by inducements of alcohol and relief shipments of white flour, sugar, and coffee as by arms and pestilence. Following the loss of their traditional way of eating, the Cherokees like other Indian communities were easily uprooted. My Daddy's fatal encounter with the Indian is a legacy of this sad chapter in American history. It is now easy for me to see how both men became imbalanced. I am no longer angry or resentful at the Indians. Of course, I would give anything to have had my Daddy alive, but from the largest possible view—that of the infinite order of the universe—I can now understand how such a tragedy could happen. I feel I have found the justice that eluded Mother but which she was seeking. I only regret that I did not know about macrobiotics sooner and was not able to help her relieve her cancer. But now I know that life is eternal and that my prayers and thoughts can help comfort and guide my parents, grandparents, and ancestors in the world of spirit and vibration.

Spread of Macrobiotics

Over the last two decades, the natural foods movement has spread throughout this country and become increasingly popular. During this same period, according to the American Heart Association, heart disease rates have fallen sharply, and the A.H.A. has consistently modified its diet in a macrobiotic direction, recommending substantial reductions in consumption of meat, eggs, dairy food, and other animal products, as well as sugar and refined foods, and corresponding increases in the consumption of whole cereal grains, vegetables, and other whole, unprocessed foods.

At Harvard Medical School and the Framingham Heart Study, scientific researchers have reported, in a series of continuing experiments, that people eating macrobiotically have the most ideal blood pressure values and cholesterol levels of any group in modern society.

The macrobiotic approach to cancer is being investigated, and the American Cancer Society is now developing dietary guidelines that bear little resemblance to the four main food groups we learned about in grade school. The A.C.S.'s dietary recommendations, "Cooking Up a Defense Against Cancer," call for substantial increases in the consumption of whole grains, vegetables, and other fresh foods.

If these trends continue, perhaps in our lifetime, we shall see the final decline of destructive modern civilization with its emphasis on technology, war, and material well-being and the beginning of a new orientation where spiritual values reign. The future society, nourished on whole grains, vegetables, and other mostly plant-quality foods, will be a society in which hostility between men and women is replaced with mutual trust, where the generation gap begins to close and young people look to their elders for wisdom and older family members extend love and care to the younger generation. It will be an era in which society begins to transform prisons from places of brutality and confinement to healing centers offering dietary and way of life counseling and training in the order of nature. Whole foods will also become widely available in hospitals and, as mental and psychological degeneration declines, people's attitudes and behavior will become more peaceful and orderly. At every level of society, we will begin to experience first-hand the contribution food can make to a healthy and harmonious world order.

Perhaps we will even see a final decline in religious and ideological teachings that divide us as a world family and a return to true spiritual teachings that contribute to a feeling of love and acceptance toward all of our brothers and sisters on the planet. East and West will become one, and North and South will mutually respect each other.

And then one day perhaps, all of us can stop worrying about working for a living and just play endlessly—doing what we want to do and going where we want to go. I hope our paths cross in the cosmic dance we are sharing and that together we can promenade home.

Recommeded Reading

Dufty, William, *Sugar Blues*, New York: Warner Books, 1975.

Esko, Wendy, *Aveline Kushi's Introducing Macrobiotic Cooking*, Tokyo & New York: Japan Publications, Inc., 1987.

Kushi, Aveline, with Alex Jack, *Aveline: The Life and Dream of the Woman Behind Macrobiotics Today*. Tokyo & New York: Japan Publications, Inc., 1988.

————, *Aveline Kushi's Complete Guide to Macrobiotic Cooking*, New York: Warner Books, 1985.

Kushi, Aveline and Michio, *Macrobiotic Pregnancy and Care of the Newborn*, edited by Edward and Wendy Esko, Tokyo & New York: Japan Publications, Inc., 1984.

————, *Macrobiotic Child Care and Family Health*, Tokyo & New York: Japan Publications, Inc., 1986.

Kushi, Aveline, with Wendy Esko, *The Changing Seasons Macrobiotic Cookbook*, Wayne, N. J.: Avery Publishing Group, 1983.

————, *Macrobiotic Family Favorites*, Tokyo & New York: Japan Publications, Inc., 1987.

Kushi, Michio, *The Book of Dō-In: Exercise for Physical and Spiritual Development*, Tokyo & New York: Japan Publications, Inc., 1979.

————, *Crime and Diet*, Tokyo & New York: Japan Publications, Inc., 1987.

————, *How to See Your Health: The Book of Oriental Diagnosis*, Tokyo & New York: Japan Publications, Inc., 1980.

Kushi, Michio, with Alex Jack, *The Book of Macrobiotics*, Tokyo & New York: Japan Publications, Inc., revised edition, 1987.

————, *The Cancer-Prevention Diet*, New York: St. Martin's Press, 1983.

————, *Diet for a Strong Heart*, New York: St. Martin's Press, 1987.

————, *One Peaceful World*, New York: St. Martin's Press, 1987.

Kushi, Michio and Aveline, with Alex Jack, *Macrobiotic Diet*, Tokyo & New York: Japan Publications, Inc., 1985.

Nussbaum, Elaine, *Recovery: From Cancer to Health through Macrobiotics*, Tokyo & New York: Japan Publications, Inc., 1986.

Robbins, John, *Diet for a New America*, Walpole, N. H.: Stillpoint Publishing, 1987.

Sattilaro, Anthony, M.D., with Tom Monte, *Recalled by Life: The Story of My Recovery from Cancer*, Boston: Houghton-Mifflin, 1982.

Yamamoto, Shizuko, *Barefoot Shiatsu*, Tokyo & New York: Japan Publications, Inc. 1979.

Resources

Gale and Alex Jack offer seminars and cooking classes, and give dietary and way of life consultations around the country.

The authors welcome your comments and reflections on this book. A special edition of *Promenade Home*, narrated by Gale, is available on audio cassette tape. For further information, please contact:

> Gale and Alex Jack
> Box 696
> Brookline Village, Mass. 02147

For further information on macrobiotic education and activities in Boston and elsewhere in the United States, Canada, or around the world, please contact:

> The Kushi Institute
> Box 1100
> Brookline, Mass. 02147
> (617) 738–0045

> Kushi Foundation Berkshire Center
> Box 7
> Becket, Mass. 01223
> (413) 623–5742